# STEPHEN LEACOCK'S

## *Laugh Parade*

*Butler*

# STEPHEN LEACOCK'S

# *Laugh Parade*

A new collection of the wit and humor of
Stephen Leacock

DODD, MEAD & COMPANY
NEW YORK          1940

Published, October, 1940
Second printing, December, 1940

PRINTED IN THE U. S. A. BY
Quinn & Boden Company, Inc.
BOOK MANUFACTURERS
RAHWAY. NEW JERSEY

# Preface

CHARLES DICKENS used to talk to "his readers" as if he owned them, and would tell them what they ought to like and why. I can't rise up to that. But I can at least express my thanks to my readers for their appreciation in the past and invite them to try a little more. When a dinner is enjoyed one offers the guests a second helping, and even presses it upon them. So do I now.

For myself, I am all in favour of reading things over again. It carries one back to one's own past life in the remembrance of the earlier reading. I have for myself such an anthology of favourite pieces, one here, one there, scattered over sixty years. I like every now and then to take a return trip with Huck Finn down the Mississippi, to recall our first journey together. I still go to the moon with Jules Verne, and ride again over what was once the Prairie. I can even wander through a lot of sawdust for what it has meant to me in the past.

So it is that for my own books I can wish no better fate than such remembrance and such reperusal. To some of my readers, now growing old, these little pieces may connect back with the light and laughter of earlier years and happier times. "We read that one day at school," says one, and laughter rises at the recollection. "I read that out loud," says another, "when we were engaged,"—and pauses at the remembrance, wondering if what he did were wise. Most of all have I liked to hear the words, "The nurse read that to me in the hospital, and the doctor warned her to be careful."

v

So with that I may easily put these reprinted pieces into the hands of their friends, with best wishes for the pleasant memories that they may recall.

STEPHEN LEACOCK

*The Old Brewery Bay*
*Orillia*

# Contents

# STEPHEN
# LEACOCK'S
*Laugh*
*Parade*

# What I Don't Know About the Drama

*(With grateful recognition of the indulgence of the various Dramatic Clubs who have heard me explain it.)*

I AM to talk tonight on the subject: What I Don't Know About the Drama. The Chairman has just wittily described this as a very wide subject. I had intended to use this joke myself if the Chairman hadn't got so smart about it. As a matter of fact he had a look at my notes before we came to the platform and I explained this one to him, and when he got it as best he could, he said it was quite funny and said he must remember it. He did.

However, let that pass. Let me first, before giving you my personal views on the drama, explain very briefly my qualifications for the task. I am what may be described as a finished actor—finished about twenty years ago. And my long and varied experience on the stage, before being finally persuaded to leave it, has served me as a background of practical knowledge as a dramatist or playwright.

I don't mean to imply that I have ever acted in any of the great Metropolitan centres. I never have. I have never even acted in my home city of Montreal. But I have acted in Verdun, the suburb where the Provincial Asylum is. The inmates were wild over my work. They wanted me to stay. They saw no reason why I shouldn't.

Nor have I ever acted in Boston. But I have acted just outside of it, in Chelsea, where the police limits end. In fact, generally speaking, wherever the police limits end, I begin.

A lot of my earlier work was done with a touring company, one of a chain of companies acting in that grand old drama *Uncle Tom's Cabin*. I am sure you all know it so well that I needn't describe the plot to you. In any case I couldn't; I wasn't part of the plot. My work was in the great climax scene, where the fugitive slave girl, Eliza, her unborn babe in her arms, is fleeing across the Ohio—leaping from one ice floe to another in the swollen flood of the river. That's where I acted—I was a chunk of ice in the Ohio, the third one from the Kentucky side, working under a blue curtain.

I put my heart into it. I said to myself: "If I am to be ice, I'll be the most dangerous ice in the river. If Eliza puts her foot on me, up she goes!" Well, I worked away conscientiously night after night until it happened one night the general manager of our chain of companies was down front. And he saw my work and he said: "*Who* is that ice? The third from Kentucky?" And they told him, and he sent for me and he said: "Look, I've seen your work. You're too good for ice. How would you like to be First Bloodhound!"

That was my first big move up. And after that I had a number of parts, not exactly character parts in the different plays but what you might call "Key-parts," the ones you see written in the stage directions. I have been *A voice is heard without,* and *A bell rings,* and I've been a Groan, and an Explosion, and a Fairy, and, of course, Thunder and Lightning ever so many times. And I've been in Shakespeare as a Tucket—you know how it says: *Enter the Duke of Burgundy with a Tucket*—and I've been a Link—*Enter the Duke of Gloucester with a Link*—and a Hobo—*Enter Belgium with Hoboes*. I am afraid my language is getting technical, but I won't apologize as

I know that the members of your club are themselves technicians.

From those earlier experiences I moved along into what has always been to me a favourite field, the old-fashioned melodrama. The play I was in was one of those typical melodramas of the New England coast, called *Cast up by the Sea*, or *Thrown up by the Waves,* or something like that—anyway one of those Foam and Storm plays of the New England seaside that used to be so popular. There was a lighthouse in it, and the lighthouse keeper was a farmer, and his daughter Liz had run away with a young man, a sea captain, and gone to sea, months before; and this night, when the play reaches its height in the third act, there's a great storm raging, and Liz and her husband, on their ship (He's captain of it.), are going to be wrecked right there beside the lighthouse.

It's a wild night in the third act. There's a group of fisherman-farmers all in oilskins down on the shore looking out to sea. One points and says, "There's lightning in yon cloud!" There wasn't. It was me. The speech was my cue for the first lightning. After that I gave it to them at three-minute intervals.

At that minute there comes a shout from the clustered fishermen on the Fore Shore.

"A ship! A ship! There's a vessel out on the reef. See! Look!"

They run up and down, pointing and shouting. And far out on the waves, lit for a moment by a flash of lightning, the audience sees a dismasted schooner (She's made of cardboard.) out beside the breakers on the reef.

.     .     .     .     .     .     .     .

Then in a vivid flash of lightning, a double charge, they get a full view of the ship out on the rocks (It was *white* cardboard and showed up well.) and they recognize it and all begin to shout, "It's the *Good Hope*." You see that was the schooner that Liz ran away in with her husband, the captain of it.

Then someone shouts: "She's struck the reef. She's breaking. They're lowering the boat. Look! Look! There's a woman in the boat!"

They all have to keep terribly excited and run up and down and get in the road of the wind, as I made it—there wasn't enough for everybody unless they kept moving.

Then they shout: "Fetch Hiram Haycroft! There's only him can pilot the lifeboat to the reef!"

Then someone else says: "He's at the light! He can't leave the light!" And a lot of them yell, "He *must* leave the light!"

And at that minute Haycroft's wife, Liz's mother, lets a shriek out of her: "It's Liz! It's Liz!" And the crowd yell, "Now he must come," and rush in a mass for the door leading up to the lighthouse. And just as they do it, you see the boat and Liz vanishing in white foam from a calcium light on the reef. . . .

Then came a sudden change of scene—all done in three minutes, from the shore to Lighthouse Tower. It was what used to be called a "transformation scene." It involved an eclipse of darkness punctured by little gas jets, and a terrible thumping and bumping with an undertone of curses. You could hear a voice in the darkness say quite distinctly, "Get that blank blank drop over there," and you could see black figures running round in the transformation. Then there came an awful crash and a vision of a back curtain sliding down amongst the dark men. The lights flicked up again and all the audience broke into applause at the final wonder of it.

Look! It's the lighthouse tower with the big lights

burning and the storm howling outside.  How bright and clear it is here inside the tower, with its great windows looking out over the storm, sixty feet above the sea.

He stands beside the lights, trimming the lamps, calm and steady at his task.  The storm is all about him, but inside the lighthouse tower all is bright and still.  Hiram peers a moment from the lighthouse window.  He opens the little door and steps out on the iron platform high above the sea.  The wind roars about him and the crest of the driven water leaps to his very feet.  I threw it.  He comes in, closing the door quietly and firmly behind him and turns again to his light.

"God help all poor souls at sea tonight," he says.  That was my cue to throw a bucketful right at him.

And then with a rush and clatter of feet they burst in upon him, the group of fishermen, Martha his wife, crowding into the lighthouse tower and standing on the stairs.

"Quick, Hiram, you must come!  There's been a wreck. Look, there's a boat going on the reef.  The men are ready in the lifeboat.  You must steer her through.  It's life or death.  There's not a moment to lose."

Hiram looks for a moment at the excited crowd and then turns quietly to his task.

"My place is here," he says.

There is a moment's hush.  Martha rushes to him and clutches him by the coat.

"Hiram, they haven't told you.  The schooner that was wrecked tonight is the *Good Hope*."

Hiram staggers back against the wall.

"And the boat that's drifting on the reef, it's Liz, it's our daughter."

Hiram stands grasping the rail along the wall.  He speaks panting with agitation, but firm:

"Martha—I'm sworn to tend the light.  If the light

fails, God knows what it means to the ships at sea.   If my child is lost, it is God's will—but—my place is here."

And he turns back to the light.

.    .    .    .    .    .    .

That was the signal for a double flash of lightning, two cylinders of thunder and a bucket right at him.

That's the kind of climax we used to love to have in the old Melodrama—everything apparently hopelessly lost and then sudden salvation.

Martha, the farmer's wife, points to a great coil of rope which her quick intelligence has perceived hanging on the wall of the tower.   As a matter of fact it was so big and so obvious that even the people in the gallery seats had noticed it right away.

"The rope!" she says.   "The rope!"

Hiram turns.

"You're right," he says.   "There's that one chance." With a fisherman's quickness of hand he ties a bowline knot at the end of the rope.   Then he throws open the door and slips out onto the iron platform in the great roar of wind and sea—that needed two of us, one for the wind, one for the sea.

The audience see the long rope go hissing out into the night air, and when Hiram hauls it up again what do you think is on the end of it?—Liz!

Her husband drowned?   Oh, no, he got him on the next throw and some of their valises but not all of them. And the play ended in a flood of happy reconciliations, with the storm all gone (I shut it right off after the second valise.) and sunrise—the dawn of a new life—just appearing in the west, where the sun had set earlier in the act.

So that was the good old Melodrama of forty years ago,

when some of us were forty years younger than we are now. We still look back to it with affection. Let me try to contrast it with the High Brow Drama of today. Forty years ago the theatre was carried on by straight hand-to-hand acting. The actors were well-armed, determined people and they fought the play through. Of course, they took their lives in their hands; they were liable to be drowned, shot, or blown up anywhere in act II, III, or IV. It always seemed a miracle that they were still alive in act V, with the dead body of the villain smoking on the floor, the missing will found, and the heroine clasped in the hero's arms, which went once and a half around her.

This used to be called Melodrama and it was played, at its best, at ten-twenty-thirty cents. Any lift in the price put a false polish on it and spoiled it.

They say that the old Melodrama is still there if you know where to find it. But for most of us, whether we like it or not, its place is being taken by the new High Brow Drama. These two dramas, the High Brow and the Melo, are wide apart. The new High Brow is not exactly played in the theatres. At least it is "given" in Little Theatres, Repertory Theatres, Community Theatres, College Auditoriums, and places like that.

The old Melodrama needed nothing but lots of sawdust, chewing tobacco, and bright open gas lights. It didn't even need fire escapes. If the audience got burned, that was too bad, but there were lots more.

The new High Brow is played among soft lights, huge ferns, heavy curtains, dim corridors, and attendants with dark lanterns.

The old Melo was played for money, just straight-out money. It had no artistic purpose whatsoever; any of the actors was ready for murder or suicide or infanticide—ready, in fact, for anything, for money.

But the new High Brow Drama is not put on for money. It is done in connection with town-planning, park-making, slum-killing, children's welfare, and maternity hospitals. The people who play it don't care about money; the people who write it are too artistic to think of money.

That's why the prices are what they are—not the old ten-twenty-thirty (infants in arms free), but seats at one-dollar-fifty, two-dollars and two-fifty. In fact you had better pay two-fifty and be done with it. You see you have to go; either your daughter is acting in it, or your friend's sister wrote it, or your son-in-law staged it. All the town is caught in the same net. So there you are in your two-fifty seat in your local Community Repertory Theatre, waiting for it to begin. Don't hurry it. It will start in an hour or so. The old Melo began on time; because the actors had their supper at the hotel at six o'clock and had nowhere else to go. But the new Repertory Community takes a lot of starting.

But even when it does start, somehow there seems something wrong with it, at least for those of us who remember the old Melo of forty years ago. It all seems too—how shall I call it?—too quiet. There's not enough *action* to it. The people in it do too much talk—just talk all the time, they never get down to business.

For instance, take the first act. There's the heroine on the stage with a man. You can't exactly make out who he is because there's no decent gas light and you can't see to read the program. But it doesn't matter. All he does and all she does is just *talk*. In the old play, if the fair heroine was left alone with a man, he was supposed to start something—either tie her by the feet and throw her out the window, or else soak her with chloroform. This got the play off to a good start. But in the new Community-Repertory-Art-for-Art's-Sake the heroine is perfectly safe. The fellow isn't man enough to lay a hand on her.

So presently the man goes out and the heroine is left alone. Here again notice the difference. In the Melodrama if the heroine had been left alone in that room she would have started skipping around, looking in every drawer and corner to find a missing will or a document to prove that her mother had been really married. But instead of that she just stays in the room alone, *analyzing* herself. She is, so it seems, trying to realize herself; in fact she distinctly says that she is trying to reconstruct her life. This leaves the audience very vague as to how she is doing it and what it is that she wants to do.

Now another character comes in. As he enters, for a moment the audience think that something is going to happen. But nothing does. The new man seems to have the same talk-mania as the one who went out. He, too, is working out some "problem." All the characters in a new Community Park and Playgrounds Theatre play are full of "problems" up to the neck.

Just once in this scene there is a piece of tense thrilling action. The man actually lights a cigarette with a match and smokes it. All the audience hope to heaven he'll set himself on fire. But he gets away with it. Once again as he goes on talking, talking, talking, another piece of action comes in. The man rings a bell and a butler comes in with cocktails. That's a dirty one on the audience. They don't get any.

But the butler is supposed to be one of the great hits of the play. He just comes in and says, "Cocktails, sir?" and goes out again. But he goes out so perfectly, and is so completely gone when he goes, that it is felt to be a fine piece of acting. If the audience of today had ever seen a train wreck in act III of the old Melo, or "road agents" hold up a stagecoach in the Rocky Mountains in act IV, they'd know what acting really can reach to.

You see the point of the old play was that things not only happened, but they kept on happening more and more. Finally they reached a terrific climax. The hero, for example, had been shot dead by the train wreckers, who had ridden off with the loot, and the heroine had been tied down across the railway track for the next train to run over her. In fact things looked pretty gloomy. Even a trained audience began to feel uneasy about the situation. Especially so, when they heard the clang of an engine bell and realized that a train was approaching over a long cardboard trestle bridge two miles away, with a twist in it.

The engine comes in sight. You can see the engineer and the fireman leaning out of the cab, but they don't see the heroine. Then just at that moment the hero—he's not dead but he's fixed up the slings and bandages to show how near dead he must have been—makes a flying leap from the rocks of the embankment into the cab of the locomotive. He grabs the throttle and tears it out by the roots. The speed slackens. The hero dashes forward onto the cowcatcher, leans away ahead with a knife in his hand, severs the heroine's bonds, and swings her into safety.

The whole theatre rocks with enthusiasm. After that, the killing of the bandits in a mountain cave with nitrogen bombs is simplicity itself. In the cave, after the explosion, are found all the necessary marriage certificates, birth certificates, lost wills and other missing documents. The play only needs a mountain marriage with a comic clergyman to cork it up tight and end it.

Now I don't see why we couldn't keep some of these features of the good old ten-twenty-thirty by incorporating them in the modern Little Theatre Play. I admit that we need the Little Community Repertory Maternity Theatre. After all Art is Art, and if we *never* get on to it, where shall we be? And anyway, town planning is a good thing, and if you don't support a Maternity Hospital what sort of man are you?

But just as a suggestion, why shouldn't the characters of the up-to-date talk play do all their analyzing and talking as part of the real action in a real play? For example let the heroine get tied down across the rails and *then* let her start to analyze herself; *then* let her try to think things out, to ascertain just how to fit in with her new environment.

While she is at it, let the train come along. Of course I admit that in the High Brow play it mustn't come fast; they've a lot of talking to get through first. We mustn't break what is called the continuity of it, or, if we do, the artistic harmony all goes to smithereens. So here is the engineer sitting in the cab with the fireman quietly talking about differential freight rates and the difference between cost of service and operating charges. Once perhaps we might let the engineer say, "I sometimes ask myself, Wilfrid, what I would do if I ran over a woman." That will give the audience a real thrill—as close to it as we dare let them come. After that the engineer will heave a deep sigh and start a game of chess with the fireman.

Now at this juncture without danger of being too crude, or too inartistic, I think we can let the hero quietly enter the cab and sit down on the steam pipes. Let him begin to talk with the engineer about predestination and whether individual will power is dependent on mass impulse—or not. Now the engineer may say: "Speaking of prestidigitation, I have a queer presentiment that I am about to run over a woman. I think I'll go and look."

While he is gone the fireman starts a talk, about fire. The engineer comes back and sits down and says gloomily that there *is* a woman on the track but that the speed of the train is slackening so fast that it is losing half its remaining velocity with each half minute.   They are half as near to the woman as they were half a minute ago but he reckons that that's about as near as you can ever say you got to a woman.

With that the curtain falls and the play ends on just that strange note of uncertainty, that perplexing unanswered questioning—that alone makes great drama.   The Germans call it, I think, *Weltschmerz*.   I forget what the Turks call it—probably much the same.

.    .    .    .    .    .    .

You will have realized from what I have said about reconstructing the melodrama to turn it into a High Brow play, that I am speaking from experience as a playwright.   I don't say that my plays have been much acted or indeed acted at all.   But that is in their favour.   They can't be acted.   It is recognized that many of the greatest dramatic works are not acting plays, and indeed hardly even *reading* plays—they are just plays.   Mine are like that.

I remember very distinctly my first success with Melodrama.   I took the manuscript to a manager.

"Where is the first act laid?" he asked.

"In a lighthouse," I answered.

"Good, and where is the second laid?"

"In a madhouse."

"Fine, and where have you laid the third act?"

"In a monkey house."

"And the fourth?"

"In the House of Lords."

"First rate," he said, "all of it, but you have forgotten to put a condemned cell, and a crypt, and a vault, and London Bridge at midnight."

"All right," I said. "Give it me back: I'll add four more acts and another set of actors acting in two shifts."

But in the end they couldn't use it. They couldn't cast it—didn't know where to throw it.

# Frenzied Fiction

*First Lecture.  Murder at $2.50 a Crime*

I PROPOSE tonight, ladies and gentlemen, to deal with murder.  There are only two subjects that appeal nowadays to the general public, murder and sex; and, for people of culture, sex-murder.  Leaving out sex for the minute—if you can—I propose tonight to talk about murder as carried on openly and daily at two dollars and fifty cents a crime.

For me, I admit right away that if I'm going to pay two dollars and fifty cents for a book I want to make sure that there's going to be at least *one* murder in it.  I always take a look at the book first to see if there's a chapter headed "Finding of the Body."  And I know that everything is all right when it says, *The body was that of an elderly gentleman, well dressed but upside down.*  Always, you notice, an "elderly gentleman."  What they have against us, I don't know.  But you see, if it said that the body was that of a woman—that's a tragedy.  The body was that of a child!—that's a horror.  But *the body was that of an elderly gentleman*—oh, pshaw! that's all right.  Anyway he's had his life—he's had a good time (It says he's well dressed.)—probably been out on a hoot.  (He's found upside down.)  That's all right!  He's worth more dead than alive.

· · · · · · ·

But as a matter of fact, from reading so many of these stories I get to be such an expert that I don't have to wait for the finding of the body.  I can tell just by a glance at

14

the beginning of the book who's going to *be* the body. For example, if the scene is laid on this side of the water, say in New York, look for an opening paragraph that runs about like this:

*Mr. Phineas Q. Cactus sat in his downtown office in the drowsy hour of a Saturday afternoon. He was alone. Work was done for the day. The clerks were gone. The building, save for the janitor, who lived in the basement, was empty.*

Notice that, *save for the janitor*. Be sure to save him. We're going to need him later on, to accuse him of the murder.

*As he sat thus, gazing in a sort of reverie at the papers on the desk in front of him, his chin resting on his hand, his eyes closed and slumber stole upon him.*

Of course! To go to sleep like that in a downtown deserted office is a crazy thing to do in New York—let alone Chicago. Every intelligent reader knows that Mr. Cactus is going to get a crack on the cocoanut. He's the body.

.        .        .        .        .        .        .

But if you don't mind my saying so, they get a better setting for this kind of thing in England than they do with us. You need an old country to get a proper atmosphere around murder. The best murders (always of elderly gentlemen) are done in the country at some old country seat—any wealthy elderly gentleman has a seat—called by such a name as the Priory, or the Doggery, or the Chase—that sort of thing.

Try this for example:

*Sir Charles Althorpe sat alone in his library at Althorpe Chase. It was late at night. The fire had burned low in the grate. Through the heavily curtained windows no sound came from outside. Save for the maids, who slept in a distant wing, and save for the butler, whose pantry was under the stairs, the Chase, at this time of the year, was empty. As Sir Charles sat thus in his arm-chair, his head gradually sank upon his chest and he dozed off into slumber.*

Foolish man! Doesn't he know that to doze off into slumber in an isolated country house, with the maids in a distant wing, is little short of madness? But do you notice?—*Sir* Charles! He's a baronet. That's the touch to give class to it. And do you notice that we have *saved* the butler, just as we did the janitor? Of course he didn't really kill Sir Charles, but the local police always arrest the butler. And anyway, he'd been seen sharpening a knife on his pants in his pantry and saying, "I'll do for the old Devil yet."

. . . . . . .

So there is the story away to a good start—Sir Charles's Body found next morning by a "terrified" maid—all maids are terrified—who "could scarcely give an intelligent account of what she saw"—they never can. Then the local police (Inspector Higginbottom of the Hopshire Contabulary) are called in and announce themselves "baffled." Every time the reader hears that the local police are called in he smiles an indulgent smile and knows they are just there to be baffled.

. . . . . . .

At this point of the story enters the Great Detective, specially sent by or through Scotland Yard. That's another high class touch—Scotland Yard. It's not a Yard, and it's not in Scotland. Knowing it only from detective fictions I imagine it is a sort of club somewhere near the Thames in London. You meet the Prime Minister and the Archbishop of Canterbury going in and out all the time —but so strictly incognito that you don't know that it is them, I mean that they are it. And apparently even "royalty" is found "closeted" with heads at the Yard— "royalty" being in English a kind of hush-word for things too high up to talk about.

Well, anyway, the Yard sends down the Great Detective, either as an official or as an outsider to whom the Yard appeal when utterly stuck; and he comes down to the Chase, looking for clues.

Here comes in a little technical difficulty in the narration of the story. We want to show what a wonderful man the Great Detective is, and yet he can't be made tell the story himself. He's too silent—and too strong. So the method used nowadays is to have a sort of shadow along with him, a companion, a sort of Poor Nut, full of admiration but short on brains. Ever since Conan Doyle started this plan with Sherlock and Watson, all the others have copied it. So the story is told by this secondary person. Taken at his own face value he certainly is a Poor Nut. Witness the way in which his brain breaks down utterly and is set going again by the Great Detective. The scene occurs when the Great Detective begins to observe all the things around the place that were overlooked by Inspector Higginbottom.

*"But how," I exclaimed, "how in the name of all that is incomprehensible, are you able to aver that the criminal wore rubbers?"*

*My friend smiled quietly.*

*"You observe," he said, "that patch of fresh mud about
ten feet square in front of the door of the house. If you
would look, you will see that it has been freshly walked
over by a man with rubbers on."*

*I looked. The marks of the rubbers were there plain
enough—at least a dozen of them.*

*"What a fool I was!" I exclaimed. "But at least tell
me how you were able to know the length of the criminal's
foot?"*

*My friend smiled again, his same inscrutable smile.*

*"By measuring the print of the rubber," he answered
quietly, "and then subtracting from it the thickness of
the material multiplied by two."*

*"Multiplied by two!" I exclaimed. "Why by two?"*

*"For the toe and the heel."*

*"Idiot that I am," I cried, "it all seems so plain when
you explain it."*

In other words, the Poor Nut makes an admirable nar-
rator. However much fogged the reader may get, he has
at least the comfort of knowing that the Nut is far more
fogged than he is. Indeed, the Nut may be said, in a
way, to personify the ideal reader, that is to say the stupidest—the reader who is most completely bamboozled with
the mystery, and yet intensely interested.

Such a reader has the support of knowing that the police
are entirely "baffled"—that's always the word for them;
that the public are "mystified"; that the authorities are
"alarmed"; the newspapers "in the dark"; and the Poor
Nut, altogether up a tree. On those terms, the reader can
enjoy his own ignorance to the full.

Before the Great Detective gets to work, or rather while
he is getting to work, the next thing is to give him *character, individuality*. It's no use to say that he "doesn't in

the least look like a detective." Of course not. No detective ever does. But the point is not what he doesn't look like, but what he does look like.

Well, for one thing, though it's pretty stale, he can be made extremely thin, in fact, "cadaverous." Why a cadaverous man can solve a mystery better than a fat man it is hard to say; presumably the thinner a man is, the more acute is his mind. At any rate, the old school of writers preferred to have their detectives lean. This incidentally gave the detective a face "like a hawk," the writer not realizing that a hawk is one of the stupidest of animals. A detective with a face like an orang-outang would beat it all to bits.

Indeed, the Great Detective's face becomes even more important than his body. Here there is absolute unanimity. His face has to be "inscrutable." Look at it though you will, you can never read it. Contrast it, for example, with the face of Inspector Higginbottom, of the local police force. Here is a face that can look "surprised," or "relieved," or, with great ease, "completely baffled."

But the face of the Great Detective knows of no such changes. No wonder the Poor Nut is completely mystified. From the face of the great man you can't tell whether the cart in which they are driving jolts him or whether the food at the Inn gives him indigestion.

To the Great Detective's face there used to be added the old-time expedient of not allowing him either to eat or drink. And when it was added that during this same period of about eight days the sleuth never slept, the reader could realize in what fine shape his brain would be for working out his "inexorable chain of logic."

But nowadays this is changed. The Great Detective not only eats, but he eats well. Often he is presented as a connoisseur in food. Thus:

*"Stop a bit." Thus speaks the Great Detective to the Poor Nut and Inspector Higginbottom, whom he is dragging round with him as usual. "We have half an hour before the train leaves Paddington. Let us have some dinner. I know an Italian restaurant near here where they serve frogs' legs à la Marengo better than anywhere else in London."*

*A few minutes later we were seated at one of the tables of a dingy little eating place whose sign board with the words "Restauranto Italiano" led me to the deduction that it was an Italian restaurant. I was amazed to observe that my friend was evidently well known in the place, while his order for "three glasses of Chianti with two drops of vermicelli in each," called for an obsequious bow from the appreciative padrone. I realized that this amazing man knew as much of the finesse of Italian wines as he did of playing the saxophone.*

We may go further. In many up-to-date cases the detective not only gets plenty to eat but a liberal allowance of strong drink. One generous British author of today is never tired of handing out to the Great Detective and his friends what he calls a "stiff whiskey and soda." At all moments of crisis they get one.

For example, when they find the body of Sir Charles Althorpe, late owner of Althorpe Chase, a terrible sight, lying on the floor of the library, what do they do? They reach at once to the sideboard and pour themselves out a "stiff whiskey and soda." It certainly is a great method.

But in the main we may say that all this stuff about eating and drinking has lost its importance. The Great Detective has to be made exceptional by some other method.

And here is where his music comes in. It transpires—

not at once but in the first pause in the story—that this great man not only can solve a crime, but has the most extraordinary aptitude for music, especially for dreamy music of the most difficult kind. As soon as he is left in the Inn room with the Poor Nut, out comes his saxophone and he tunes it up.

*"What were you playing?"* I asked, as my friend at last folded his beloved instrument into its case.
*"Beethoven's Sonata in Q,"* he answered modestly.
*"Good Heavens!"* I exclaimed.

.     .     .     .     .     .     .

Up to this point the story, any detective story, has been a howling success. The body has been found; they're all baffled and full of whiskey and soda, and everything's fine! But the only trouble is how to go on with it! You can't! There's no way to make crime really interesting except at the start; it's a pity they have to go on, that they can't just stay baffled and full, and call it a day.

But now begin the mistakes and the literary fallacies that spoil a crime story. At this point in comes the heroine—the heroine!—who has no real place in a murder story but is just a left-over remnant of the love story. In she comes, Margaret Althorpe, wild and all dishevelled. No wonder she's wild! Who wouldn't be? And dishevelled—oh, yes, the best writers always dishevel them up like that. In she comes, almost fainting! What do they do, Inspector Higginbottom and the Great Detective? They shoot a "stiff whiskey and soda" into her—and hit one themselves at the same time.

.     .     .     .     .     .     .

And with that, you see, the story drifts off sideways so as to work up a love-interest in the heroine, who has

no business in it at all.  Making a heroine used to be an
easy thing in earlier books when the reading public was
small.  The author just imagined the kind of girl that he
liked himself and let it go at that.  Walter Scott, for example, liked them small—size three—"sylph-like" was the
term used; in fact the heroine was just a "slip of a girl"—
the slippier the better.

But Margaret Althorpe has to please everybody at once.
So the description of her runs like this:

*Margaret Althorpe was neither short nor tall.*

—That means that she looked pretty tall standing up
but when she sat down she was sawed off.

*. . . Her complexion neither dark nor fair, and her
religion was neither Protestant nor Roman Catholic.  She
was not a prohibitionist but never took more than a couple
of gins at a time.  Her motto was, "No, boys, that's all
I can hold."*

That at least is about the spirit of the description.  But
even at that, description of what is called her "person" is
not sufficient by itself.  There is the question of her "temperament" as well.  Unless a heroine has "temperament"
she can't get by; and temperament consists in undergoing
a great many physiological changes in a minimum of time.
Here, for example, are the physiological variations under-
gone by the heroine of a book I read the other day, in
what appeared to be a space of seventeen minutes:

*A new gladness ran through her.*

> . . . . . .

*A thrill coursed through her* (presumably in the oppo-
site direction).

> . . . . . .

*Something woke up within her that had been dead.*

. . . . . . .

*A great yearning welled up within her.*

. . . . . . .

*Something seemed to go out from her that was not of her nor to her.*

. . . . . . .

*Everything sank within her.*

That last means, I think, that something had come unhooked.

. . . . . .

But, you see, by this turn the novel has reached what the diplomats call an *impasse,* and plainer people simply a *cul de sac* or a *ne plus ultra.* It can't get on. They arrested the butler. He didn't do it. Apparently nobody did it.

In other words all detective stories reach a point where the reader gets impatient and says to himself: "Come now; *somebody* murdered Sir Charles! Out with it." And the writer has no answer. All the old attempts at an answer suitable for literary purposes have been worn thin. There used to be a simple and easy solution of a crime mystery by finding that the murder was done by a "tramp." In the old Victorian days the unhappy creature called a tramp had no rights that the white man had to respect, either in fiction or out of it. They'd hang a tramp as unconcernedly as they'd catch a butterfly. And if he belonged to the class called a "villainous-looking tramp" he registered as A.1., and his execution (indicated but not described) was part of the happy ending, along with Margaret Althorpe's marriage to the Poor Nut as a by-product on the side—not of course to the Great Detective. Marriage is not for him.  He passes on to the next mystery, in which "royalty" itself is deeply concerned.

.    .    .    .    .    .

But all the tramp stuff is out of date.  With a hundred million people "on the dole" and on "relief," we daren't set them to work at murder.  We have to get another solution.

Here is one, used for generations but still going fairly strong.  The murderer is found; oh, yes, he's found all right and confesses his guilt, *but* it is only too plain that his physical condition is such that he must soon "go before a higher tribunal."  And that doesn't mean the supreme court.

It seems that at the moment when the Great Detective and Inspector Higginbottom have seized him he has developed a "hacking cough."  This is one of those terrible maladies known only in fiction—like "brain fever" and a "broken heart," for which all medicine is in vain.  Indeed in this case, as the man starts to make his confession, he can hardly talk for hacks.

*"Well," said Garth, looking round at the little group of police officers, "the game is up—hack! hack!—and I may as well make a clean breast of it—hack, hack, hack."*

Any trained reader when he hears these hacks knows exactly what they are to lead up to.  The criminal, robust though he seemed only a chapter ago when he jumped through a three-story window after throttling Sub-Inspector Juggins half to death, is a dying man.  He has got one of those terrible diseases known to fiction as a "mortal complaint."  It wouldn't do to give it an exact name, or somebody might get busy and cure it.  The symptoms are a hacking cough and a great mildness of manner, an absence of all profanity, and a tendency to call everybody "you gentlemen." Those things spell finis.

In fact, all that is needed now is for the Great Detective himself to say, *"Gentlemen"* (They are all gentlemen at this stage of the story.), *"a higher conviction than any earthly law has, et cetera, et cetera."* With that, the curtain is dropped, and it is understood that the criminal made his exit the same night.

That's better, decidedly better. And yet, lacking in cheerfulness, somehow.

In fact this solution has something a little cowardly about it. It doesn't face the music.

One more of these futile solutions may be offered. Here's the way it is done.

*The Great Detective stood looking about him, quietly shaking his head. His eye rested a moment on the prostrate body of Sub-Inspector Bradshaw, then turned to scrutinize the neat hole drilled in the glass of the window.*

*"I see it all now," he murmured. "I should have guessed it sooner. There is no doubt whose work this is."*

*"Who is it?" I asked.*

*"Blue Edward," he announced quietly.*

*"Blue Edward!" I exclaimed.*

*"Blue Edward," he repeated.*

*"Blue Edward!" I reiterated, "but who then is Blue Edward?"*

This, of course, is the very question that the reader is wanting to ask. Who on earth is Blue Edward? The question is answered at once by the Great Detective himself.

*"The fact that you have never heard of Blue Edward merely shows the world that you have lived in. As a*

*matter of fact, Blue Edward is the terror of four conti-
nents. We have traced him to Shanghai, only to find him
in Madagascar. It was he who organized the terrible robbery at Irkutsk in which ten mujiks were blown up with
a bottle of Epsom salts.*

*"It was Blue Edward who for years held the whole of
Philadelphia in abject terror, and kept Oshkosh, Wisconsin,
on the jump for even longer. At the head of a gang of
criminals that ramifies all over the known globe, equipped
with a scientific education that enables him to read and
write and use a typewriter with the greatest ease, Blue
Edward has practically held the police of the world at bay
for years.*

*"I suspected his hand in this from the start. From the
very outset, certain evidences pointed to the work of
Blue Edward."*

After which all the police inspectors and spectators keep
shaking their heads and murmuring, "Blue Edward, Blue
Edward," until the reader is sufficiently impressed.

.    .    .    .    .    .    .

The fact is that the writer *can't* end the story, not if
it is sufficiently complicated in the beginning. No possible ending satisfies the case. Not even the glad news
that the heroine sank into the Poor Nut's arms, never to
leave them again, can relieve the situation. Not even the
knowledge that they erected a handsome memorial to Sir
Charles, or that the Great Detective played the saxophone
for a week can quite compensate us.

# "We Have With Us To-night"

NOT only during my tour in England but for many years past it has been my lot to speak and to lecture in all sorts of places, under all sorts of circumstances and before all sorts of audiences. I say this, not in boastfulness, but in sorrow. Indeed, I only mention it to establish the fact that when I talk of lecturers and speakers, I talk of what I know.

Few people realise how arduous and how disagreeable public lecturing is. The public sees the lecturer step out on to the platform in his little white waistcoat and his long tailed coat and with a false air of a conjurer about him, and they think him happy. After about ten minutes of his talk they are tired of him. Most people tire of a lecture in ten minutes; clever people can do it in five. Sensible people never go to lectures at all. But the people who do go to a lecture and who get tired of it, presently hold it as a sort of a grudge against the lecturer personally. In reality his sufferings are worse than theirs.

For my own part I always try to appear as happy as possible while I am lecturing. I take this to be part of the trade of anybody labelled a humourist and paid as such. I have no sympathy whatever with the idea that a humourist ought to be a lugubrious person with a face stamped with melancholy. This is a cheap and elementary effect belonging to the level of a circus clown. The image of "laughter shaking both his sides" is the truer picture of comedy. Therefore, I say, I always try to appear cheerful at my lectures and even to laugh at my own jokes. Oddly enough this arouses a kind of resentment in some

27

of the audience. "Well, I will say," said a stern-looking woman who spoke to me after one of my lectures, "you certainly do seem to enjoy your own fun." "Madam," I answered, "if I didn't, who would?" But in reality the whole business of being a public lecturer is one long variation of boredom and fatigue. So I propose to set down here some of the many trials which the lecturer has to bear.

The first of the troubles which any one who begins giving public lectures meets at the very outset is the fact that the audience won't come to hear him. This happens invariably and constantly, and not through any fault or shortcoming of the speaker.

I don't say that this happened very often to me in my tour in England. In nearly all cases I had crowded audiences: by dividing up the money that I received by the average number of people present to hear me I have calculated that they paid thirteen cents each. And my lectures are evidently worth thirteen cents. But at home in Canada I have very often tried the fatal experiment of lecturing for nothing: and in that case the audience simply won't come. A man will turn out at night when he knows he is going to hear a first class thirteen cent lecture; but when the thing is given for nothing, why go to it?

The city in which I live is overrun with little societies, clubs and associations, always wanting to be addressed. So at least it is in appearance. In reality the societies are composed of presidents, secretaries and officials, who want the conspicuousness of office, and a large list of other members who won't come to the meetings. For such an association, the invited speaker who is to lecture for nothing prepares his lecture on "Indo-Germanic Factors in the Current of History." If he is a professor, he takes all the winter at it. You may drop in at his house at any time and his wife will tell you that he is "upstairs working on his lecture." If he comes down at all it is in carpet slippers and dressing gown. His mental vision of his meeting is that of a huge gathering of keen people with Indo-Germanic faces, hanging upon every word.

Then comes the fated night. There are seventeen people present. The lecturer refuses to count them. He refers to them afterwards as "about a hundred." To this group he reads his paper on the Indo-Germanic Factor. It takes him two hours. When he is over the chairman invites discussion. There is *no* discussion. The audience is willing to let the Indo-Germanic factors go unchallenged. Then the chairman makes his speech. He says:

"I am very sorry indeed that we should have had such a very poor 'turn out' to-night. I am sure that the members who were not here have missed a real treat in the delightful paper that we have listened to. I want to assure the lecturer that if he comes to the Owl's Club again we can guarantee him next time a capacity audience. And will any members, please, who haven't paid their dollar this winter, pay it either to me or to Mr. Sibley as they pass out."

I have heard this speech (in the years when I have had to listen to it) so many times that I know it by heart. I have made the acquaintance of the Owl's Club under so many names that I recognise it at once. I am aware that its members refuse to turn out in cold weather; that they do not turn out in wet weather; that when the weather is really fine, it is impossible to get them together; that the slightest counter-attraction,—a hockey match, a sacred concert,—goes to their heads at once.

There was a time when I was the newly appointed occupant of a college chair and had to address the Owl's Club. It is a penalty that all new professors pay; and the Owls batten upon them like bats. It is one of the compensations

of age that I am free of the Owl's Club forever.  But in
the days when I still had to address them, I used to take it
out of the Owls in a speech, delivered, in imagination only
and not out loud, to the assembled meeting of the seventeen Owls, after the chairman had made his concluding
remarks.  It ran as follows:

"Gentlemen—if you are such, which I doubt.  I realise
that the paper which I have read on 'Was Hegel a deist?'
has been an error.  I spent all the winter on it and now
I realise that not one of you pups know who Hegel was
or what a deist is.  Never mind.  It is over now, and I
am glad.  But just let me say this, only this, which won't
keep you a minute.  Your chairman has been good enough
to say that if I come again you will get together a capacity
audience to hear me.  Let me tell you that if your society
waits for its next meeting till I come to address you again,
you will wait indeed.  In fact, gentlemen—I say it very
frankly—it will be in another world."

But I pass over the audience.  Suppose there is a real
audience, and suppose them all duly gathered together.
Then it becomes the business of that gloomy gentleman—
facetiously referred to in the newspaper reports as the
"genial chairman"—to put the lecturer to the bad.  In
nine cases out of ten he can do so.  Some chairmen, indeed,
develop a great gift for it.  Here are one or two examples
from my own experience:

"Ladies and gentlemen," said the chairman of a society
in a little country town in Western Ontario, to which I
had come as a paid (a very humbly paid) lecturer, "we
have with us to-night a gentleman" (here he made an attempt to read my name on a card, failed to read it and
put the card back in his pocket)—"a gentleman who is to
lecture to us on" (here he looked at his card again)—"on
Ancient—Ancient,—I don't very well see what it is—

Ancient—Britain? Thank you, on Ancient Britain. Now, this is the first of our series of lectures for this winter. The last series, as you all know, was not a success. In fact, we came out at the end of the year with a deficit. So this year we are starting a new line and trying the experiment of cheaper talent."

Here the chairman gracefully waved his hand toward me and there was a certain amount of applause. "Before I sit down," the chairman added, "I'd like to say that I am sorry to see such a poor turn-out to-night and to ask any of the members who haven't paid their dollar to pay it either to me or to Mr. Sibley as they pass out."

Let anybody who knows the discomfiture of coming out before an audience on any terms, judge how it feels to crawl out in front of them labelled *cheaper talent*.

Another charming way in which the chairman endeavours to put both the speaker for the evening and the audience into an entirely good humour, is by reading out letters of regret from persons unable to be present. This, of course, is only for grand occasions when the speaker has been invited to come under very special auspices. It was my fate, not long ago, to "appear" (this is the correct word to use in this connection) in this capacity when I was going about Canada trying to raise some money for the relief of the Belgians. I travelled in great glory with a pass on the Canadian Pacific Railway (not since extended: officials of the road kindly note this) and was most generously entertained wherever I went.

It was, therefore, the business of the chairman at such meetings as these to try and put a special distinction or cachet on the gathering. This is how it was done:

"Ladies and gentlemen," said the chairman, rising from his seat on the platform with a little bundle of papers in his hand, "before I introduce the speaker of the evening,

I have one or two items that I want to read to you." Here he rustles his papers and there is a deep hush in the hall while he selects one. "We had hoped to have with us to-night Sir Robert Borden, the Prime Minister of this Dominion. I have just received a telegram from Sir Robert in which he says that he will not be able to be here" (*great applause*). The chairman puts up his hand for silence, picks up another telegram and continues, "Our committee, ladies and gentlemen, telegraphed an invitation to Sir Wilfrid Laurier very cordially inviting him to be here to-night. I have here Sir Wilfrid's answer in which he says that he will not be able to be with us" (*renewed applause*). The chairman again puts up his hand for silence and goes on, picking up one paper after another. "The Minister of Finance regrets that he will be unable to come" (*applause*). "Mr. Rodolphe Lemieux (*applause*) will not be here (*great applause*)—the Mayor of Toronto (*applause*) is detained on business (*wild applause*)—the Anglican Bishop of the Diocese (*applause*)—the Principal of the University College, Toronto (*great applause*)—the Minister of Education (*applause*)—none of these are coming." There is a great clapping of hands and enthusiasm, after which the meeting is called to order with a very distinct and palpable feeling that it is one of the most distinguished audiences ever gathered in the hall.

Here is another experience of the same period while I was pursuing the same exalted purpose: I arrived in a little town in Eastern Ontario, and found to my horror that I was billed to "appear" *in a church*. I was supposed to give readings from my works, and my books are supposed to be of a humorous character. A church hardly seemed the right place to get funny in. I explained my difficulty to the pastor of the church, a very solemn looking man. He nodded his head, slowly and gravely, as he grasped my difficulty. "I see," he said, "I see, but I think that I can introduce you to our people in such a way as to make that right."

When the time came, he led me up on to the pulpit platform of the church, just beside and below the pulpit itself, with a reading desk and a big bible and a shaded light beside it. It was a big church, and the audience, sitting in half darkness, as is customary during a sermon, reached away back into the gloom. The place was packed full and absolutely quiet. Then the chairman spoke:

"Dear friends," he said, "I want you to understand that it will be all right to laugh to-night. Let me hear you laugh heartily, laugh right out, just as much as ever you want to, because" (and here his voice assumed the deep sepulchral tones of the preachers),—"when we think of the noble object for which the professor appears to-night, we may be assured that the Lord will forgive any one who will laugh at the professor."

I am sorry to say, however, that none of the audience, even with the plenary absolution in advance, were inclined to take a chance on it.

I recall in this same connection the chairman of a meeting at a certain town in Vermont. He represents the type of chairman who turns up so late at the meeting that the committee have no time to explain to him properly what the meeting is about or who the speaker is. I noticed on this occasion that he introduced me very guardedly by name (from a little card) and said nothing about the Belgians, and nothing about my being (supposed to be) a humourist. This last was a great error. The audience, for want of guidance, remained very silent and decorous, and well behaved during my talk. Then, somehow, at the end, while some one was moving a vote of thanks, the chairman discovered his error. So he tried to make it good. Just as the audience were getting up to put on their wraps, he rose, knocked on his desk and said:

"Just a minute, please, ladies and gentlemen, just a minute. I have just found out—I should have known it sooner, but I was late in coming to this meeting—that the speaker who has just addressed you has done so in behalf of the Belgian Relief Fund. I understand that he is a well-known Canadian humourist (ha! ha!) and I am sure that we have all been immensely amused (ha! ha!). He is giving his delightful talks (ha! ha!)—though I didn't know this till just this minute—for the Belgian Relief Fund, and he is giving his services for nothing. I am sure when we realise this, we shall all feel that it has been well worth while to come. I am only sorry that we didn't have a better turn-out to-night. But I can assure the speaker that if he will come again, we shall guarantee him a capacity audience. And I may say, that if there are any members of this association who have not paid their dollar this season, they can give it either to myself or to Mr. Sibley as they pass out."

With the amount of accumulated experience that I had behind me I was naturally interested during my lecture in England in the chairmen who were to introduce me. I cannot help but feel that I have acquired a fine taste in chairmen. I know them just as other experts know old furniture and Pekinese dogs. The witty chairman, the prosy chairman, the solemn chairman,—I know them all. As soon as I shake hands with the chairman in the Committee room I can tell exactly how he will act.

There are certain types of chairmen who have so often been described and are so familiar that it is not worth while to linger on them. Everybody knows the chairman who says,—"Now, ladies and gentlemen, you have not come here to listen to *me*. So I will be very brief; in fact,

I will confine my remarks to just one or two very short observations." He then proceeds to make observations for twenty-five minutes. At the end of it he remarks with charming simplicity, "Now I know that you are all impatient to hear the lecturer. . . ."

And everybody knows the chairman who comes to the meeting with a very imperfect knowledge of who or what the lecturer is, and is driven to introduce him by saying:

"Our lecturer of the evening is widely recognised as one of the greatest authorities on,—on,—on his subject in the world to-day. He comes to us from,—from a great distance and I can assure him that it is a great pleasure to this audience to welcome a man who has done so much to,—to,—to advance the interests of,—of,—of everything as he has."

But this man, bad as he is, is not so bad as the chairman whose preparation for introducing the speaker has obviously been made at the eleventh hour. Just such a chairman it was my fate to strike in the form of a local alderman, built like an ox, in one of those small manufacturing places in the north of England where they grow men of this type and elect them into office.

"I never saw the lecturer before," he said, "but I've read his book." (I have writen nineteen books.) "The committee was good enough to send me over his book last night. I didn't read it all but I took a look at the preface and I can assure him that he is very welcome. I understand he comes from a college. . . ." Then he turned directly towards me and said in a loud voice, "What was the name of that college over there you said you came from?"

"McGill," I answered equally loudly.

"He comes from McGill," the chairman boomed out. "I never heard of McGill myself but I can assure him he's welcome. He's going to lecture to us on,—what did you say it was to be about?"

"It's a humorous lecture," I said.

"Ay, it's to be a humorous lecture, ladies and gentlemen, and I'll venture to say it will be a rare treat. I'm only sorry I can't stay for it myself as I have to get back over to the Town Hall for a meeting. So without more ado I'll get off the platform and let the lecturer go on with his humour."

A still more terrible type of chairman is one whose mind is evidently preoccupied and disturbed with some local happening and who comes on to the platform with a face imprinted with distress. Before introducing the lecturer he refers in moving tones to the local sorrow, whatever it is. As a prelude to a humorous lecture this is not gay.

Such a chairman fell to my lot one night before a gloomy audience in a London suburb.

"As I look about this hall to-night," he began in a doleful whine, "I see many empty seats." Here he stifled a sob. "Nor am I surprised that a great many of our people should prefer to-night to stay quietly at home—"

I had no clue to what he meant. I merely gathered that some particular sorrow must have overwhelmed the town that day.

"To many it may seem hardly fitting that after the loss our town has sustained we should come out here to listen to a humorous lecture,—"

"What's the trouble?" I whispered to a citizen sitting beside me on the platform.

"Our oldest resident"—he whispered back—"he died this morning."

"How old?"

"Ninety-four," he whispered.

Meantime the chairman, with deep sobs in his voice, continued:

"We debated in our committee whether or not we should have the lecture. Had it been a lecture of another character our position would have been less difficult,—"

By this time I began to feel like a criminal.

"The case would have been different had the lecture been one that contained information, or that was inspired by some serious purpose, or that could have been of any benefit. But this is not so. We understand that this lecture which Mr. Leacock has already given, I believe, twenty or thirty times in England,—"

Here he turned to me with a look of mild reproval while the silent audience, deeply moved, all looked at me as at a man who went around the country insulting the memory of the dead by giving a lecture thirty times.

"We understand, though this we shall have an opportunity of testing for ourselves presently, that Mr. Leacock's lecture is not of a character which,—has not, so to speak, the kind of value,—in short, is not a lecture of that class."

Here he paused and choked back a sob.

"Had our poor friend been spared to us for another six years he would have rounded out the century. But it was not to be. For two or three years past he has noted that somehow his strength was failing, that, for some reason or other, he was no longer what he had been. Last month he began to droop. Last week he began to sink. Speech left him last Tuesday. This morning he passed, and he has gone now, we trust, in safety to where there are no lectures."

The audience were now nearly in tears.

The chairman made a visible effort towards firmness and control.

"But yet," he continued, "our committee felt that in

another sense it was our duty to go on with our arrangements. I think, ladies and gentlemen, that the war has taught us all that it is always our duty to 'carry on,' no matter how hard it may be, no matter with what reluctance we do it, and whatever be the difficulties and the dangers, we must carry on to the end: for after all there is an end and by resolution and patience we can reach it.

"I will, therefore, invite Mr. Leacock to deliver to us his humorous lecture, the title of which I have forgotten, but I understand it to be the same lecture which he has already given thirty or forty times in England."

But contrast with this melancholy man the genial and pleasing person who introduced me, all upside down, to a metropolitan audience.

He was so brisk, so neat, so sure of himself that it didn't seem possible that he could make any kind of a mistake. I thought it unnecessary to coach him. He seemed absolutely all right.

"It is a great pleasure,"—he said, with a charming, easy appearance of being entirely at home on the platform,— "to welcome here to-night our distinguished Canadian fellow citizen, Mr. Learoyd"—he turned half way towards me as he spoke with a sort of gesture of welcome, admirably executed. If only my name had been Learoyd instead of Leacock it would have been excellent.

"There are many of us," he continued, "who have awaited Mr. Learoyd's coming with the most pleasant anticipations. We seemed from his books to know him already as an old friend. In fact I think I do not exaggerate when I tell Mr. Learoyd that his name in our city has long been a household word. I have very, very great pleasure, ladies and gentlemen, in introducing to you Mr. Learoyd."

As far as I know that chairman never knew his error. At the close of my lecture he said that he was sure that the audience "were deeply indebted to Mr. Learoyd," and then with a few words of rapid, genial apology buzzed off, like a humming bird, to other avocations.   But I have amply forgiven him: anything for kindness and geniality; it makes the whole of life smooth.   If that chairman ever comes to my home town he is hereby invited to lunch or dine with me, as Mr. Learoyd or under any name that he selects.

Such a man is, after all, in sharp contrast to the kind of chairman who has no native sense of the geniality that ought to accompany his office.   There is, for example, a type of man who thinks that the fitting way to introduce a lecturer is to say a few words about the finances of the society to which he is to lecture (for money) and about the difficulty of getting members to turn out to hear lectures.

Everybody has heard such a speech a dozen times.   But it is the paid lecturer sitting on the platform who best appreciates it.   It runs like this:

"Now, ladies and gentlemen, before I invite the lecturer of the evening to address us there are a few words that I would like to say.   There are a good many members who are in arrears with their fees.   I am aware that these are hard times and it is difficult to collect money but at the same time the members ought to remember that the expenses of the society are very heavy.   The fees that are asked by the lecturers, as I suppose you know, have advanced very greatly in the last few years.   In fact I may say that they are becoming almost prohibitive."

This discourse is pleasant hearing for the lecturer.   He can see the members who have not yet paid their annual dues eyeing him with hatred.   The chairman goes on:

"Our finance committee were afraid at first that we could not afford to bring Mr. Leacock to our society.   But fortunately through the personal generosity of two of our members who subscribed ten pounds each out of their own pocket we are able to raise the required sum."

(*Applause: during which the lecturer sits looking and feeling like the embodiment of the "required sum."*)

"Now, ladies and gentlemen," continues the chairman, "what I feel is that when we have members in the society who are willing to make this sacrifice,—because it is a sacrifice, ladies and gentlemen,—we ought to support them in every way. The members ought to think it their duty to turn out to the lectures. I know that it is not an easy thing to do. On a cold night, like this evening, it is hard, I admit it is hard, to turn out from the comfort of one's own fireside and come and listen to a lecture. But I think that the members should look at it not as a matter of personal comfort but as a matter of duty towards this society. We have managed to keep this society alive for fifteen years and, though I don't say it in any spirit of boasting, it has not been an easy thing to do. It has required a good deal of pretty hard spade work by the committee. Well, ladies and gentlemen, I suppose you didn't come here to listen to me and perhaps I have said enough about our difficulties and troubles. So without more ado (this is always a favourite phrase with chairmen) I'll invite Mr. Leacock to address the society,—oh, just a word before I sit down. Will all those who are leaving before the end of the lecture kindly go out through the side door and step as quietly as possible? Mr. Leacock."

Anybody who is in the lecture business knows that that introduction is far worse than being called Mr. Learoyd.

When any lecturer goes across to England from this side of the water there is naturally a tendency on the part of the chairman to play upon this fact. This is especially true in the case of a Canadian like myself. The chairman feels that the moment is fitting for one of those great imperial thoughts that bind the British Empire together. But sometimes the expression of the thought falls short of the full glory of the conception.

Witness this (word for word) introduction that was used against me by a clerical chairman in a quiet spot in the south of England:

"Not so long ago, ladies and gentlemen," said the vicar, "we used to send out to Canada various classes of our community to help build up that country. We sent out our labourers, we sent out our scholars and professors. Indeed we even sent out our criminals. And now," with a wave of his hand towards me, "they are coming back."

There was no laughter. An English audience is nothing if not literal; and they are as polite as they are literal. They understood that I was a reformed criminal and as such they gave me a hearty burst of applause.

But there is just one thing that I would like to chronicle here in favour of the chairman and in gratitude for his assistance. Even at his worst he is far better than having no chairman at all. Over in England a great many societies and public bodies have adopted the plan of "cutting out the chairman." Wearying of his faults, they have forgotten the reasons for his existence and undertaken to do without him.

The result is ghastly. The lecturer steps up on to the platform alone and unaccompanied. There is a feeble ripple of applause; he makes his miserable bow and explains with as much enthusiasm as he can who he is. The atmosphere of the thing is so cold that an Arctic expedition isn't in it with it. I found also the further difficulty that in the absence of the chairman very often the audience, or a large part of it, doesn't know who the lecturer is. On many occasions I received on appearing a wild burst of applause under the impression that I was somebody else. I have been mistaken in this way for Mr. Briand, then Prime Minister of France, for Charlie Chaplin, for Mrs. Asquith,—but stop, I may get into a libel suit. All I mean is that without a chairman "we celebrities" get terribly mixed up together.

To one experience of my tour as a lecturer I shall always be able to look back with satisfaction. I nearly had the pleasure of killing a man with laughing: and this in the most literal sense. American lecturers have often dreamed of doing this. I nearly did it. The man in question was a comfortable apoplectic-looking man with the kind of merry rubicund face that is seen in countries where they don't have prohibition. He was seated near the back of the hall and was laughing uproariously. All of a sudden I realised that something was happening. The man had collapsed sideways on to the floor; a little group of men gathered about him; they lifted him up and I could see them carrying him out, a silent and inert mass. As in duty bound I went right on with my lecture. But my heart beat high with satisfaction. I was sure that I had killed him. The reader may judge how high these hopes rose when a moment or two later a note was handed to the chairman who then asked me to pause for a moment in my lecture and stood up and asked, "Is there a doctor in the audience?" A doctor rose and silently went out. The lecture continued; but there was no more laughter; my aim had now become to kill another of them and they knew it. They were aware that if they started laughing they might die. In a few minutes a second note was handed to the chairman. He announced very gravely, "A second doctor is wanted." The lecture went on in deeper silence than ever. All the audience were waiting for a third announcement. It came. A new message was handed to the chairman. He rose and said, "If Mr. Murchison, the undertaker, is in the audience, will he kindly step outside."

That man, I regret to say, got well. Disappointing though it is to read it, he recovered. I sent back next morning from London a telegram of enquiry (I did it in reality so as to have a proper proof of his death) and received the answer, "Patient doing well; is sitting up in bed and reading Lord Haldane's *Relativity;* no danger of relapse."

# Why I Am Leaving My Farm

*I Can't Live Up to It*

(*A Lunch Club Talk that was designed to stop the Back to the Land Movement. It killed it dead.*)

MY! But these farmers are wonderful fellows—I mean the words they use and the education they must have! I never realized it till just recently when I retired from being a professor and came to settle down on my little place that I call a farm.

I hadn't had anything to do with a farm since I lived on one as a little boy, more than fifty years ago. I am amazed at the change! I'm not sufficiently educated for it. I'll have to go back to the city.

I mean like this—a few days ago I bought a bottle of poison to use against garden bugs, and it had on the label, "The antidote to this poison is any alkali emetic followed by an emollient febrifuge"! Just think of it! Imagine a farmer's wife calling downstairs: "William! Baby has been eating shoeblacking! Throw me up an alkali emetic and follow it with an emollient febrifuge!" And the farmer would probably call back: "All right! And you'd better handle baby very carefully. Lift him up with callipers!"

That's another word on farmers' labels, "callipers"; directions for all seeds and things say, "Handle very carefully and pick up with a pair of callipers." Up till now I always thought that callipers were French things that women wear. But it seems not. . . .

Anyway you have to have them on a farm. I'm going to get measured for a pair right away.

This high standard of education—I mean this need of knowledge of special terms—makes it hard for any outsider to start in and do anything around the house and garden. You see, on a farm, everything is done from printed directions, either out of little manuals or from papers that come with the packet or round the bottle or under the wrapper.

When I took over my place, as it was meant to be my home for good, I thought I would begin by planting trees round it for shelter. From what I remember of farming when I was young, I naturally thought of spruce trees, and balsam and pine—any kind of fir trees. But it seems they don't have them. The book said, "The snuggest effect about the dwelling house is to be got by having a warm belt of *conifers* about it." I don't want them. All I remember about conifers, if I have the word right, is that if they once get into the frame of a bed or bedroom chest of drawers all you can do is to burn it. You can of course try poison, any good unguent or emollient, but it seldom works. The conifers could be lifted out one by one by callipers, but it would take a lot of time. The book says, "If set out when quite young they will increase rapidly." I don't doubt it, but, thank you, not for me.

The same manual suggested that if a belt of conifers was not available an equally snug effect can be made by covering the loggia with eucalyptus. "Loggia" is a new word for me, though I suppose I can guess what it refers to. Personally I would just give it a coat of whitewash.

I have found already that gardening has to go the same way as planting trees. I don't understand the words. Try this:

"Nitrates may be freely used with leguminous plants"

. . . "at the time of calyx closing watch closely for cur-
culio" . . . "remember that the ranunculus is the gar-
dener's friend" . . . "among the birds all the caprimul-
gidae are well worth having, while the flickers wage war
on larvae" . . . etc.  It seems that farmers eat up this
kind of language by the paragraph.

There was an old man working in the next lot to my
place on the first day of gardening, and I asked him what
he thought of the weather.  In the days when I was young
such an old man would have said:

"Well, sir, if them clouds would clear away off the sun
for a bit I think it might set in for a pretty fair spell."

But this old man didn't.

He said:

"I had a look at my aneroid barometer first thing this
morning and there is certainly an area of pretty low baro-
metric pressure.  I had been thinking of setting some
antirrhinum this morning, but I guess I won't."

"Why not?" I asked.

"It's too aquaceous.  You've got to keep a pretty good
eye on your humidity gauge before you do much with
antirrhinum.  I'll put in something a little more gelatinous."

Think of it.  That old man getting out of bed and having a look at his aneroid before he even put on his pants.

I was going to ask him what he would do instead of
setting out antirrhinum, but then I didn't.  I didn't need
to.  I knew what he would do.

He would go out and start to do all those things that
are in the Farm and Home Manuals and on the seed packets and that I can't understand.  For instance, he might
go and make himself "a compost bed."  Don't ask me
what it is; I've no idea, except that it is said to be a grand
thing to make with an eye to the future.  "Soap suds,

dirty water and all kinds of kitchen slops thrown on the compost bed will help to keep it in good heart." It sounds like a dirty enough mess.

Or if the old man didn't make a compost bed, then he might spend his time "treating his soil" with nitrate, phosphorus or basic slag. "What are they?" I don't know. "Where do you get basic slag?" I have no idea.

Then, if the old man had done that, he could go and plant his garden—with what, do you think—lettuce, radishes and that sort of stuff that I had expected to grow?—not at all. They don't have them any more. He could plant it with antirrhinum, as I have just said, and scabies, and cuspis and a border of asbestos and scrofula. Those are the words on the packets, as nearly as I recall them.

So, as for gardening, I'm out of it. I don't understand the terms.

"When the garden is complete," suggests the manual, "a final touch may be given by laying down a flagstone path, with saxifrage in the interstices, and then having a pergola all down the pathway." Thank you, not for me.

Another thing I had looked forward to in coming back to farm life, after fifty years away from it, was the reading of the good old farm newspapers. They've been parodied, I know, a thousand times by smart city people; but the charm was there all the same. There was personal news that said, "Ed Callaghar was in town last night from the Fourth Concession and reports his fall wheat nicely in hand. Well done! Ed"; and the social news, "Miss Posie Cowslip of Price's Corners is home after a three days' visit in the city."

In the place of that you now read:

"Among the daintiest of the season's weddings was that of Miss Poinsettia Primrose, celebrated at the family Farmstead, The Bagnolias, the happy bridegroom being Mr.

Earl DeBenture of Wall Street. The ceremony, at which the Rev. Mr. Bray officiated, was held out of doors under a pergola, the assembled guests being gathered in the loggia, beautified with floral decorations of bubiscus, rabies and flowering avunculus. Miss Primrose wore a beautiful écrin of soft tulle shot with dainty écrus. Her father, who gave her away, wore a plain vignolette of haricot while Mrs. Primrose (mère) looked riante in a dark purple chassis de nacre. The happy couple left immediately after the ceremony for a wedding tour through the Panama Canal to Japan, returning via Soviet Russia."

.   .   .   .   .   .   .

I find I don't talk much to the neighbors. I can't. One of them, a young farmer from near by, dropped in the other day to ask if I could lend him a pair of callipers to reset his seismograph, and we had a little talk. He talked a little while on surrealism which he said had been interesting him lately; he spoke also of metampsychosis and then drifted onto foreign politics and the "open door" in Manchuria. I think it was in Manchuria; it may have been Missouri.

.   .   .   .   .   .   .

No, no. I'll have to go back and study a whole lot more and learn all about alkalis and barometers and callipers: or else perhaps not come to the country but retire into a beer garden. It's easier.

# The Man in Asbestos: An Allegory of the Future

To begin with let me admit that I did it on purpose. Perhaps it was partly from jealousy.

It seemed unfair that other writers should be able at will to drop into a sleep of four or five hundred years, and to plunge head-first into a distant future and be a witness of its marvels.

I wanted to do that too.

I always had been, I still am, a passionate student of social problems. The world of today with its roaring machinery, the unceasing toil of its working classes, its strife, its poverty, its war, its cruelty, appals me as I look at it. I love to think of the time that must come some day when man will have conquered nature, and the toil-worn human race enter upon an era of peace.

I loved to think of it, and I longed to see it.

So I set about the thing deliberately.

What I wanted to do was to fall asleep after the customary fashion, for two or three hundred years at least, and wake and find myself in the marvel world of the future.

I made my preparations for the sleep.

I bought all the comic papers that I could find, even the illustrated ones. I carried them up to my room in my hotel: with them I brought up a pork pie and dozens and dozens of doughnuts. I ate the pie and the doughnuts, then sat back in the bed and read the comic papers one after the other. Finally, as I felt the awful lethargy stealing upon me, I reached out my hand for the *London Weekly Times,* and held up the editorial page before my eye.

It was, in a way, clear, straight suicide, but I did it.

I could feel my senses leaving me. In the room across the hall there was a man singing. His voice, that had been loud, came fainter and fainter through the transom. I fell into a sleep, the deep immeasurable sleep in which the very existence of the outer world was hushed. Dimly I could feel the days go past, then the years, and then the long passage of the centuries.

Then, not as it were gradually, but quite suddenly, I woke up, sat up, and looked about me.

Where was I?

Well might I ask myself.

I found myself lying, or rather sitting up, on a broad couch. I was in a great room, dim, gloomy, and dilapidated in its general appearance, and apparently, from its glass cases and the stuffed figures that they contained, some kind of museum.

Beside me sat a man. His face was hairless, but neither old nor young. He wore clothes that looked like the grey ashes of paper that had burned and kept its shape. He was looking at me quietly, but with no particular surprise or interest.

"Quick," I said, eager to begin; "where am I? Who are you? What year is this; is it the year 3000, or what is it?"

He drew in his breath with a look of annoyance on his face.

"What a queer, excited way you have of speaking," he said.

"Tell me," I said again, "is this the year 3000?"

"I think I know what you mean," he said; "but really

I haven't the faintest idea. I should think it must be at least that, within a hundred years or so; but nobody has kept track of them for so long, it's hard to say."

"Don't you keep track of them any more?" I gasped.

"We used to," said the man. "I myself can remember that a century or two ago there were still a number of people who used to try to keep track of the year, but it died out along with so many other faddish things of that kind. Why," he continued, showing for the first time a sort of animation in his talk, "what was the use of it? You see, after we eliminated death—"

"Eliminated death!" I cried, sitting upright. "Good God!"

"What was that expression you used?" queried the man.

"Good God!" I repeated.

"Ah," he said, "never heard it before. But I was saying that after we had eliminated Death, and Food, and Change, we had practically got rid of Events, and—"

"Stop!" I said, my brain reeling. "Tell me one thing at a time."

"Humph!" he ejaculated. "I see, you must have been asleep a long time. Go on then and ask questions. Only, if you don't mind, just as few as possible, and please don't get interested or excited."

Oddly enough the first question that sprang to my lips was—

"What are those clothes made of?"

"Asbestos," answered the man. "They last hundreds of years. We have one suit each, and there are billions of them piled up, if anybody wants a new one."

"Thank you," I answered. "Now tell me where I am?"

"You are in a museum. The figures in the cases are specimens like yourself. But here," he said, "if you want really to find out about what is evidently a new epoch to you, get off your platform and come out on Broadway and sit on a bench."

I got down.

As we passed through the dim and dust-covered buildings I looked curiously at the figures in the cases.

"By Jove!" I said, looking at one figure in blue clothes with a belt and baton, "that's a policeman!"

"Really," said my new acquaintance, "is *that* what a *policeman* was? I've often wondered. What used they to be used for?"

"Used for?" I repeated in perplexity. "Why, they stood at the corner of the street."

"Ah, yes, I see," he said, "so as to shoot at the people. You must excuse my ignorance," he continued, "as to some of your social customs in the past. When I took my education I was operated upon for social history, but the stuff they used was very inferior."

I didn't in the least understand what the man meant, but had no time to question him, for at that moment we came out upon the street, and I stood riveted in astonishment.

Broadway! Was it possible? The change was absolutely appalling! In place of the roaring thoroughfare that I had known, this silent, moss-grown desolation. Great buildings fallen into ruin through the sheer stress of centuries of wind and weather, the sides of them coated over with a growth of fungus and moss! The place was soundless. Not a vehicle moved. There were no wires overhead—no sound of life or movement except, here and there, there passed slowly to and fro human figures dressed in the same asbestos clothes as my acquaintance, with the same hairless faces, and the same look of infinite age upon them.

Good heavens! And was this the era of the Conquest

that I had hoped to see! I had always taken for granted, I do not know why, that humanity was destined to move forward. This picture of what seemed desolation on the ruins of our civilisation rendered me almost speechless.

There were little benches placed here and there on the street. We sat down.

"Improved, isn't it," said the man in asbestos, "since the days when you remember it?"

He seemed to speak quite proudly.

I gasped out a question.

"Where are the street cars and the motors?"

"Oh, done away with long ago," he said; "how awful they must have been. The noise of them!" and his asbestos clothes rustled with a shudder.

"But how do you get about?"

"We don't," he answered. "Why should we? It's just the same being here as being anywhere else." He looked at me with an infinity of dreariness in his face.

A thousand questions surged into my mind at once. I asked one of the simplest.

"But how do you get back and forwards to your work?"

"Work!" he said. "There isn't any work. It's finished. The last of it was all done centuries ago."

I looked at him a moment open-mouthed. Then I turned and looked again at the grey desolation of the street with the asbestos figures moving here and there.

I tried to pull my senses together. I realised that if I was to unravel this new and undreamed-of future, I must go at it systematically and step by step.

"I see," I said after a pause, "that momentous things have happened since my time. I wish you would let me ask you about it all systematically, and would explain it to me bit by bit. First, what do you mean by saying that there is no work?"

"Why," answered my strange acquaintance, "it died out of itself. Machinery killed it. If I remember rightly, you had a certain amount of machinery even in your time. You had done very well with steam, made a good beginning with electricity, though I think radial energy had hardly as yet been put to use."

I nodded assent.

"But you found it did you no good. The better your machines, the harder you worked. The more things you had the more you wanted. The pace of life grew swifter and swifter. You cried out, but it would not stop. You were all caught in the cogs of your own machine. None of you could see the end."

"That is quite true," I said. "How do you know it all?"

"Oh," answered the Man in Asbestos, "that part of my education was very well operated—I see you do not know what I mean. Never mind, I can tell you that later. Well, then, there came, probably almost two hundred years after your time, the Era of the Great Conquest of Nature, the final victory of Man and Machinery."

"They did conquer it?" I asked quickly, with a thrill of the old hope in my veins again.

"Conquered it," he said, "beat it out! Fought it to a standstill! Things came one by one, then faster and faster, in a hundred years it was all done. In fact, just as soon as mankind turned its energy to decreasing its needs instead of increasing its desires, the whole thing was easy. Chemical Food came first. Heavens! the simplicity of it. And in your time thousands of millions of people tilled and grubbed at the soil from morning till night. I've seen specimens of them—farmers, they called them. There's one in the museum. After the invention of Chemical Food we piled up enough in the emporiums in a year to last for centuries. Agriculture went overboard. Eat-

ing and all that goes with it, domestic labour, housework
—all ended. Nowadays one takes a concentrated pill
every year or so, that's all. The whole digestive apparatus,
as you knew it, was a clumsy thing that had been bloated
up like a set of bagpipes through the evolution of its
use!"

I could not forbear to interrupt. "Have you and these
people," I said, "no stomachs—no apparatus?"

"Of course we have," he answered, "but we use it to
some purpose. Mine is largely filled with my education—
but there! I am anticipating again. Better let me go on
as I was. Chemical Food came first: that cut off almost
one-third of the work, and then came Asbestos Clothes.
That was wonderful! In one year humanity made enough
suits to last for ever and ever. That, of course, could
never have been if it hadn't been connected with the revolt of women and the fall of Fashion."

"Have the Fashions gone," I asked, "that insane, extrav-
agant idea of—" I was about to launch into one of my
old-time harangues about the sheer vanity of decorative
dress, when my eye rested on the moving figures in asbestos, and I stopped.

"All gone," said the Man in Asbestos. "Then next to
that we killed, or practically killed, the changes of cli-
mate. I don't think that in your day you properly understood how much of your work was due to the shifts of
what you called the weather. It meant the need of all
kinds of special clothes and houses and shelters, a wilderness of work. How dreadful it must have been in your
day—wind and storms, great wet masses—what did you
call them?—clouds—flying through the air, the ocean full
of salt, was it not?—tossed and torn by the wind, snow
thrown all over everything, hail, rain—how awful!"

"Sometimes," I said, "it was very beautiful. But how did you alter it?"

"Killed the weather!" answered the Man in Asbestos. "Simple as anything—turned its forces loose one against the other, altered the composition of the sea so that the top became all more or less gelatinous. I really can't explain it, as it is an operation that I never took at school, but it made the sky grey, as you see it, and the sea gum-coloured, the weather all the same. It cut out fuel and houses and an infinity of work with them!"

He paused a moment. I began to realise something of the course of evolution that had happened.

"So," I said, "the conquest of nature meant that presently there was no more work to do?"

"Exactly," he said, "nothing left."

"Food enough for all?"

"Too much," he answered.

"Houses and clothes?"

"All you like," said the Man in Asbestos, waving his hand. "There they are. Go out and take them. Of course, they're falling down—slowly, very slowly. But they'll last for centuries yet, nobody need bother."

Then I realised, I think for the first time, just what work had meant in the old life, and how much of the texture of life itself had been bound up in the keen effort of it.

Presently my eyes looked upward: dangling at the top of a moss-grown building I saw what seemed to be the remains of telephone wires.

"What became of all that," I said, "the telegraph and the telephone and all the system of communication?"

"Ah," said the Man in Asbestos, "that was what a telephone meant, was it? I knew that it had been suppressed centuries ago. Just what was it for?"

"Why," I said with enthusiasm, "by means of the telephone we could talk to anybody, call up anybody, and
talk at any distance."

"And anybody could call you up at any time and talk?"
said the Man in Asbestos, with something like horror.
"How awful! What a dreadful age yours was, to be
sure. No, the telephone and all the rest of it, all the
transportation and intercommunication was cut out and
forbidden. There was no sense in it. You see," he added,
"what you don't realise is that people after your day became gradually more and more reasonable. Take the railroad, what good was that? It brought into every town
a lot of people from every other town. Who wanted
them? Nobody. When work stopped and commerce
ended, and food was needless, and the weather killed, it
was foolish to move about. So it was all terminated. Anyway," he said, with a quick look of apprehension and a
change in his voice, "it was dangerous!"

"So!" I said. "Dangerous! You still have danger?"

"Why, yes," he said, "there's always the danger of getting broken."

"What do you mean?" I asked.

"Why," said the Man in Asbestos, "I suppose it's what
you would call being dead. Of course, in one sense there's
been no death for centuries past; we cut that out. Disease
and death were simply a matter of germs. We found
them one by one. I think that even in your day you had
found one or two of the easier, the bigger ones?"

I nodded.

"Yes, you had found diphtheria and typhoid, and, if I
am right, there were some outstanding, like scarlet fever
and smallpox, that you called ultra-microscopic, and
which you were still hunting for, and others that you
didn't even suspect. Well, we hunted them down one

by one and destroyed them. Strange that it never occurred to any of you that Old Age was only a germ! It
turned out to be quite a simple one, but it was so distributed in its action that you never even thought of it."

"And you mean to say," I ejaculated in amazement,
looking at the Man in Asbestos, "that nowadays you live
for ever?"

"I wish," he said, "that you hadn't that peculiar, excit-
able way of talking; you speak as if everything *mattered*
so tremendously. Yes," he continued, "we live for ever,
unless, of course, we get broken. That happens sometimes.
I mean that we may fall over a high place or bump on
something, and snap ourselves. You see, we're just a little
brittle still—some remnant, I suppose, of the Old Age
germ—and we have to be careful. In fact," he continued,
"I don't mind saying that accidents of this sort were the
most distressing feature of our civilisation till we took
steps to cut out all accidents. We forbid all street cars,
street traffic, aeroplanes, and so on. The risks of your
time," he said, with a shiver of his asbestos clothes, "must
have been awful."

"They were," I answered, with a new kind of pride in
my generation that I had never felt before, "but we
thought it part of the duty of brave people to—"

"Yes, yes," said the Man in Asbestos impatiently, "please
don't get excited. I know what you mean. It was quite
irrational."

We sat silent for a long time. I looked about me at
the crumbling buildings, the monotone, unchanging sky,
and the dreary, empty street. Here, then, was the fruit
of the Conquest, here was the elimination of work, the
end of hunger and of cold, the cessation of the hard struggle, the downfall of change and death—nay, the very millennium of happiness. And yet, somehow, there seemed

something wrong with it all. I pondered, then I put two or three rapid questions, hardly waiting to reflect upon the answers.

"Is there any war now?"

"Done with centuries ago. They took to settling international disputes with a slot machine. After that all foreign dealings were given up. Why have them? Everybody thinks foreigners awful."

"Are there any newspapers now?"

"Newspapers! What on earth would we want them for? If we should need them at any time there are thousands of old ones piled up. But what is in them, anyway; only things that *happen*, wars and accidents and work and death. When these went newspapers went too. Listen," continued the Man in Asbestos, "you seem to have been something of a social reformer, and yet you don't understand the new life at all. You don't understand how completely all our burdens have disappeared. Look at it this way. How used your people to spend all the early part of their lives?"

"Why," I said, "our first fifteen years or so were spent in getting education."

"Exactly," he answered; "now notice how we improved on all that. Education in our day is done by surgery. Strange that in your time nobody realised that education was simply a surgical operation. You hadn't the sense to see that what you really did was to slowly remodel, curve and convolute the inside of the brain by a long and painful mental operation. Everything learned was reproduced in a physical difference to the brain. You knew that, but you didn't see the full consequences. Then came the invention of surgical education—the simple system of opening the side of the skull and engrafting into it a piece of prepared brain. At first, of course, they had to use, I

suppose, the brains of dead people, and that was ghastly"
—here the Man in Asbestos shuddered like a leaf—"but
very soon they found how to make moulds that did just
as well. After that it was a mere nothing; an operation
of a few minutes would suffice to let in poetry or foreign
languages or history or anything else that one cared to
have. Here, for instance," he added, pushing back the
hair at the side of his head and showing a scar beneath it,
"is the mark where I had my spherical trigonometry let in.
That was, I admit, rather painful, but other things, such
as English poetry or history, can be inserted absolutely
without the least suffering. When I think of your painful,
barbarous methods of education through the ear, I shudder at it. Oddly enough, we have found lately that for a
great many things there is no need to use the head. We
lodge them—things like philosophy and metaphysics, and
so on—in what used to be the digestive apparatus. They
fill it admirably."

He paused a moment. Then went on:

"Well, then, to continue, what used to occupy your
time and effort after your education?"

"Why," I said, "one had, of course, to work, and then,
to tell the truth, a great part of one's time and feeling was
devoted toward the other sex, towards falling in love and
finding some woman to share one's life."

"Ah," said the Man in Asbestos, with real interest. "I've
heard about your arrangements with the women, but never
quite understood them. Tell me; you say you selected
some woman?"

"Yes."

"And she became what you called your wife?"

"Yes, of course."

"And you worked for her?" asked the Man in Asbestos
in astonishment.

"Yes."

"And she did not work?"

"No," I answered, "of course not."

"And half of what you had was hers?"

"Yes."

"And she had the right to live in your house and use your things?"

"Of course," I answered.

"How dreadful!" said the Man in Asbestos. "I hadn't realised the horrors of your age till now."

He sat shivering slightly, with the same timid look in his face as before.

Then it suddenly struck me that of the figures on the street, all had looked alike.

"Tell me," I said, "are there no women now? Are they gone too?"

"Oh, no," answered the Man in Asbestos, "they're here just the same. Some of those are women. Only, you see, everything has been changed now. It all came as part of their great revolt, their desire to be like the men. Had that begun in your time?"

"Only a little," I answered; "they were beginning to ask for votes and equality."

"That's it," said my acquaintance, "I couldn't think of the word. Your women, I believe, were something awful, were they not? Covered with feathers and skins and dazzling colours made of dead things all over them? And they laughed, did they not, and had foolish teeth, and at any moment they could inveigle you into one of those contracts! Ugh!"

He shuddered.

"Asbestos," I said (I knew no other name to call him), as I turned on him in wrath, "Asbestos, do you think that those jelly-bag Equalities out on the street there, with their ash-barrel suits, can be compared for one moment with our unredeemed, unreformed, heaven-created, hobble-skirted women of the twentieth century?"

Then, suddenly, another thought flashed into my mind—

"The children," I said, "where are the children? Are there any?"

"Children," he said, "no! I have never heard of there being any such things for at least a century. Horrible little hobgoblins they must have been! Great big faces, and cried constantly! And *grew*, did they not? Like funguses! I believe they were longer each year than they had been the last, and—"

I rose.

"Asbestos!" I said, "this, then, is your coming Civilisation, your millennium. This dull, dead thing, with the work and the burden gone out of life, and with them all the joy and the sweetness of it. For the old struggle— mere stagnation, and in place of danger and death, the dull monotony of security and the horror of an unending decay! Give me back," I cried, and I flung wide my arms to the dull air, "the old life of danger and stress, with its hard toil and its bitter chances, and its heart-breaks. I see its value! I know its worth! Give me no rest," I cried aloud—

.    .    .    .    .    .    .

"Yes, but give a rest to the rest of the corridor!" cried an angered voice that broke in upon my exultation.

Suddenly my sleep had gone.

I was back again in the room of my hotel, with the hum of the wicked, busy old world all about me, and loud in my ears the voice of the indignant man across the corridor.

"Quit your blatting, you infernal blatherskite," he was calling. "Come down to earth."

I came.

# Getting by at College

*A Study in How to Elude the Examiner*

(AUTHOR'S NOTE: *While I was a professor my students used often to ask me whether there was no way to get an education quicker than by the long and arduous route of study and examinations. I always refused to give away the secrets of the profession. But now that I have retired I don't mind explaining that with a little technical skill it is possible to "get by" most of the tests and examinations of school and college.*)

EVERY student should train himself to be like the conjurer Houdini. Tie him as you would, lock him in as you might, he got loose. A student should acquire this looseness.

For the *rudiments* of education there is no way round. The multiplication table has got to be learned. They say Abraham Lincoln knew it all. So, too, the parts of speech must be committed to memory, and left there. The names of the Wessex Kings, from Alfred (better Aelfrydd) to his Danish successor Half-Knut, should be learned and carefully distinguished from the branches of the Amazon.

But, these rudiments once passed, education gets easier and easier as it goes on. When one reaches the stage of being what is called a ripe scholar, it is so easy as to verge on imbecility.

Now for college examinations, once the student is let into college, there are a great number of methods of evasion. Much can always be done by sheer illegibility of handwriting, by smearing ink all over the exam paper, and then crumpling it up into a ball.

But apart from this, each academic subject can be fought on its own ground. Let me give one or two examples.

Here, first, is the case of Latin translation, the list of extracts from Caesar, Cicero, etc., the origin of each always indicated by having the word Caesar, etc., under it. On this we seize as our opportunity. The student doesn't need to know one word of Latin. He learns by heart a piece of translated Latin, selecting a typical extract, and he writes that down. The examiner merely sees a faultless piece of translation and notices nothing—or at least thinks the candidate was given the wrong extract. He lets him pass.

Here is the piece of Caesar as required.

*These things being thus this way, Caesar although not yet did he not know neither the copiousness of the enemy not whether they had frumentum, having sent on Labienus with an impediment he himself on the first day before the third day, ambassadors having been sent to Vercingetorix, lest who might which, all having been done, set out.*

*Caesar. Bum Gallicum. Op. cit.*

Cicero also is easily distinguished by the cold biting logic of his invective. Try this:—

*How now which, what, oh, Catiline, infected, infracted, disducted, shall you still perfrage us? To what expunction shall we not subject you? To what bonds, to what vinculation, to how great a hyphen? Do I speak? Does he? No.*

*Cicero. In (and through) Catiline.*

The summation of what is called the liberal arts course is reached with such subjects as political theory, philosophy, etc. Here the air is rarer and clearer and vision easy. There is no trouble at all in circling around the examiner at will. The best device is found in the use of quotations from learned authors of whom he has perhaps—indeed, very likely—never heard, and the use of languages which he either doesn't know or can't read in blurred writing. We take for granted that the examiner is a conceited, pedantic man, as they all are, and is in a hurry to finish his work and get back to a saloon.

Now let me illustrate.

Here is a question from a recent examination in Modern Philosophy. I think I have it correct or nearly so.

*"Discuss Descartes' proposition 'Cogito ergo sum' as a valid basis of epistemology."*

Answer:

*Something of the apparent originality of Descartes' dictum, "Cogito ergo sum," disappears when we recall that, long before him, Globulus had written "*Testudo ergo crepito,*" and the great Arab Scholar Alhelallover, writing about 200 Fahrenheit, has said "*Indigo ergo gum.*" But we have only to turn to Descartes' own brilliant contemporary, the Abbé Pâté de Foi Grasse, to find him writing, "*dimanche, lundi, mardi, mercredi, jeudi, vendredi, samedi,*" which means as much, or more, than Descartes' assertion. It is quite likely that the Abbé was himself acquainted with the words of Pretzel, Wiener Schnitzel and Schmierkäse; even more likely still he knew the treatise of the low German Fisch von Gestern who had already set together a definite system or schema. He writes:* Wo ist mein Bruder? Er ist in dem Hause. Habe ich den Vogel gesehen? dies ist ein gutes Mes-

SER. HOLEN SIE KARL UND FRITZ UND WIR WERDEN INS THEATER GEHEN. DANKE BESTENS.

There—one can see how easy it is. I know it from my own experience. I remember in my fourth year in Toronto (1891) going into the exam room and picking up a paper which I carelessly took for English Philology; I wrote on it, passed on it and was pleasantly surprised two weeks later when they gave me a degree in Ethnology. I had written the wrong paper. This story, oddly enough, is true.

# The Errors of Santa Claus

Iᴛ was Christmas Eve.

The Browns, who lived in the adjoining house, had been dining with the Joneses.

Brown and Jones were sitting over wine and walnuts at the table. The others had gone upstairs.

"What are you giving to your boy for Christmas?" asked Brown.

"A train," said Jones, "new kind of thing—automatic."

"Let's have a look at it," said Brown.

Jones fetched a parcel from the sideboard and began unwrapping it.

"Ingenious thing, isn't it?" he said, "goes on its own rails. Queer how kids love to play with trains, isn't it?"

"Yes," assented Brown, "how are the rails fixed?"

"Wait, I'll show you," said Jones, "just help me to shove these dinner things aside and roll back the cloth. There! See! You lay the rails like that and fasten them at the ends, so—"

"Oh, yes, I catch on, makes a grade, doesn't it? Just the thing to amuse a child, isn't it? I got Willie a toy aeroplane."

"I know, they're great. I got Edwin one on his birthday. But I thought I'd get him a train this time. I told him Santa Claus was going to bring him something altogether new this time. Edwin, of course, believes in Santa Claus absolutely. Say, look at this locomotive, would you? It has a spring coiled up inside the fire box."

"Wind her up," said Brown with great interest, "let's see her go."

67

"All right," said Jones, "just pile up two or three plates or something to lean the end of the rails on. There, notice the way it buzzes before it starts. Isn't that a great thing for a kid, eh?"

"Yes," said Brown, "and say! see this little string to pull the whistle. By Gad, it toots, eh? Just like real?"

"Now then, Brown," Jones went on, "you hitch on those cars and I'll start her. I'll be engineer, eh!"

Half an hour later Brown and Jones were still playing trains on the dining-room table.

But their wives upstairs in the drawing room hardly noticed their absence. They were too much interested.

"Oh, I think it's perfectly sweet," said Mrs. Brown, "just the loveliest doll I've seen in years. I must get one like it for Ulvina. Won't Clarisse be perfectly enchanted?"

"Yes," answered Mrs. Jones, "and then she'll have all the fun of arranging the dresses. Children love that so much. Look! there are three little dresses with the doll, aren't they cute? All cut out and ready to stitch together."

"Oh, how perfectly lovely," exclaimed Mrs. Brown, "I think the mauve one would suit the doll best—don't you? —with such golden hair—only don't you think it would make it much nicer to turn back the collar, so, and to put a little band—so?"

"*What* a good idea!" said Mrs. Jones, "do let's try it. Just wait, I'll get a needle in a minute. I'll tell Clarisse that Santa Claus sewed it himself. The child believes in Santa Claus absolutely."

And half an hour later Mrs. Jones and Mrs. Brown were so busy stitching dolls' clothes that they could not hear the roaring of the little train up and down the dining table, and had no idea what the four children were doing.

Nor did the children miss their mothers.

"Dandy, aren't they?" Edwin Jones was saying to little Willie Brown, as they sat in Edwin's bedroom. "A hundred in a box, with cork tips, and see, an amber mouthpiece that fits into a little case at the side. Good present for dad, eh?"

"Fine!" said Willie, appreciatively, "I'm giving father cigars."

"I know, I thought of cigars too. Men always like cigars and cigarettes. You can't go wrong on them. Say, would you like to try one or two of these cigarettes? We can take them from the bottom. You'll like them, they're Russian,—away ahead of Egyptian."

"Thanks," answered Willie. "I'd like one immensely. I only started smoking last spring—on my twelfth birthday. I think a feller's a fool to begin smoking cigarettes too soon, don't you? It stunts him. I waited till I was twelve."

"Me too," said Edwin, as they lighted their cigarettes. "In fact, I wouldn't buy them now if it weren't for dad. I simply *had* to give him something from Santa Claus. He believes in Santa Claus absolutely, you know."

And while this was going on, Clarisse was showing little Ulvina the absolutely lovely little bridge set that she got for her mother. "Aren't these markers perfectly charming?" said Ulvina, "and don't you love this little Dutch design—or is it Flemish, darling?"

"Dutch," said Clarisse, "isn't it quaint? And aren't these the dearest little things—for putting the money in when you play. I needn't have got them with it—they'd have sold the rest separately—but I think it's too utterly slow playing without money, don't you?"

"Oh, abominable," shuddered Ulvina, "but your mamma never plays for money, does she?"

"Mamma! Oh, gracious, no. Mamma's far too slow for that. But I shall tell her that Santa Claus insisted on putting in the little money boxes."

"I suppose she believes in Santa Claus, just as my Mamma does."

"Oh, absolutely," said Clarisse, and added, "What if we play a little game! With a double dummy, the French way, or Norwegian Skat, if you like. That only needs two."

"All right," agreed Ulvina, and in a few minutes they were deep in a game of cards with a little pile of pocket money beside them.

About half an hour later, all the members of the two families were down again in the drawing room. But of course nobody said anything about the presents. In any case they were all too busy looking at the beautiful big Bible, with maps in it, that the Joneses had bought to give to Grandfather. They all agreed that with the help of it, Grandfather could hunt up any place in Palestine in a moment, day or night.

But upstairs, away upstairs in a sitting room of his own, Grandfather Jones was looking with an affectionate eye at the presents that stood beside him. There was a beautiful whiskey decanter, with silver filigree outside (and whiskey inside) for Jones, and for the little boy a big nickel-plated Jew's harp.

Later on, far in the night, the person, or the influence, or whatever it is called Santa Claus, took all the presents and placed them in the people's stockings.

And, being blind as he always has been, he gave the wrong things to the wrong people—in fact, he gave them just as indicated above.

But the next day, in the course of Christmas morning, the situation straightened itself out, just as it always does.

Indeed, by ten o'clock, Brown and Jones were playing with the train, and Mrs. Brown and Mrs. Jones were making dolls' clothes, and the boys were smoking cigarettes, and Clarisse and Ulvina were playing cards for their pocket money.

And upstairs—away up—Grandfather was drinking whiskey and playing the Jew's harp.

And so Christmas, just as it always does, turned out all right after all.

# With the Photographer

"I WANT my photograph taken," I said. The photographer looked at me without enthusiasm. He was a drooping man in a gray suit, with the dim eye of a natural scientist. But there is no need to describe him. Everybody knows what a photographer is like.

"Sit there," he said, "and wait."

I waited an hour. I read the *Ladies Companion* for 1912, the *Girls Magazine* for 1902 and the *Infants Journal* for 1888. I began to see that I had done an unwarrantable thing in breaking in on the privacy of this man's scientific pursuits with a face like mine.

After an hour the photographer opened the inner door.

"Come in," he said severely.

I went into the studio.

"Sit down," said the photographer.

I sat down in a beam of sunlight filtered through a sheet of factory cotton hung against a frosted skylight.

The photographer rolled a machine into the middle of the room and crawled into it from behind.

He was only in it a second,—just time enough for one look at me,—and then he was out again, tearing at the cotton sheet and the window panes with a hooked stick, apparently frantic for light and air.

Then he crawled back into the machine again and drew a little black cloth over himself. This time he was very quiet in there. I knew that he was praying and I kept still.

When the photographer came out at last, he looked very grave and shook his head.

"The face is quite wrong," he said.

"I know," I answered quietly; "I have always known it."

He sighed.

"I think," he said, "the face would be better three-quarters full."

"I'm sure it would," I said enthusiastically, for I was glad to find that the man had such a human side to him. "So would yours. In fact," I continued, "how many faces one sees that are apparently hard, narrow, limited, but the minute you get them three-quarters full they get wide, large, almost boundless in—"

But the photographer had ceased to listen. He came over and took my head in his hands and twisted it sideways. I thought he meant to kiss me, and I closed my eyes.

But I was wrong.

He twisted my face as far as it would go and then stood looking at it.

He sighed again.

"I don't like the head," he said.

Then he went back to the machine and took another look.

"Open the mouth a little," he said.

I started to do so.

"Close it," he added quickly.

Then he looked again.

"The ears are *bad*," he said; "droop them a little more. Thank you. Now the eyes. Roll them in under the lids. Put the hands on the knees, please, and turn the face just a little upward. Yes, that's better. Now just expand the lungs! So! And hump the neck—that's it—and just contract the waist—ha!—and twist the hip up toward the

elbow—now!  I still don't quite like the face, it's just a
trifle *too* full, but—"

I swung myself round on the stool.

"Stop," I said with emotion but, I think, with dignity.
"This face is *my* face.  It is not yours, it is mine.  I've
lived with it for forty years and I know its faults.  I
know it's out of drawing.  I know it wasn't made for me,
but it's *my* face, the only one I have—"  I was conscious
of a break in my voice but I went on—"such as it is,
I've learned to love it.  And this is my mouth, not yours.
These ears are *mine*, and if your machine is too narrow—"
Here I started to rise from the seat.

Snick!

The photographer had pulled a string.  The photograph
taken.  I could see the machine still staggering from the
shock.

"I think," said the photographer, pursing his lips in a
pleased smile, "that I caught the features just in a moment
of animation."

"So!" I said bitingly,—"features, eh?  You didn't think
I could animate them, I suppose?  But let me see the picture."

"Oh, there's nothing to see yet," he said, "I have to
develop the negative first.  Come back on Saturday and
I'll let you see a proof of it."

On Saturday I went back.

The photographer beckoned me in.  I thought he
seemed quieter and graver than before.  I think, too, there
was a certain pride in his manner.

He unfolded the proof of a large photograph, and we
both looked at it in silence.

"Is it me?" I asked.

"Yes," he said quietly, "it is you," and we went on
looking at it.

"The eyes," I said hesitatingly, "don't look very much like mine."

"Oh, no," he answered, "I've retouched them.  They come out splendidly, don't they?"

"Fine," I said, "but surely my eyebrows are not like that?"

"No," said the photographer, with a momentary glance at my face, "the eyebrows are removed.  We have a process now—the Delphide—for putting in new ones. You'll notice here where we've applied it to carry the hair away from the brow.  I don't like the hair low on the skull."

"Oh, you don't, don't you?" I said.

"No," he went on, "I don't care for it.  I like to get the hair clear back to the superficies and make out a new brow line."

"What about the mouth?" I said with a bitterness that was lost on the photographer; "is that mine?"

"It's adjusted a little," he said, "yours is too low.  I found I couldn't use it."

"The ears, though," I said, "strike me as a good likeness; they're just like mine."

"Yes," said the photographer thoughtfully, "that's so; but I can fix that all right in the print.  We have a process now—the Sulphide—for removing the ears entirely.  I'll see if—"

"Listen!" I interrupted, drawing myself up and animating my features to their full extent and speaking with a withering scorn that should have blasted the man on the spot.  "Listen!  I came here for a photograph—a picture —something which (mad though it seems) would have looked like me.  I wanted something that would depict my face as Heaven gave it to me, humble though the gift may have been.  I wanted something that my friends might keep after my death, to reconcile them to my loss. It seems that I was mistaken. What I wanted is no longer done. Go on, then, with your brutal work. Take your negative, or whatever it is you call it,—dip it in sulphide, bromide, oxide, cowhide,—anything you like,—remove the eyes, correct the mouth, adjust the face, restore the lips, reanimate the necktie and reconstruct the waistcoat. Coat it with an inch of gloss, shade it, emboss it, gild it, till even you acknowledge that it is finished. Then when you have done all that—keep it for yourself and your friends. They may value it. To me it is but a worthless bauble."

I broke into tears and left.

# Eddie the Bartender

### *A Ghost of the Bygone Past*

THERE he stands—or rather, there he used to stand—in his wicker sleeves, behind the tall mahogany, his hand on the lever of the beer pump—Eddie the Bartender.

Neat, grave, and courteous in the morning, was Eddie. "What's yours, sir?"

Slightly subdued in the drowsier hours of the afternoon, but courteous still. "What are you having, gentlemen?"

Cheerful, hospitable, and almost convivial in the evening. "What is it this time, boys?"

. . . . . . .

All things to all men, was Eddie, quiet with the quiet, affable with the affable, cheerful with the exhilarated and the gay; in himself nothing, a perfect reflection of his customer's own mind.

"Have one yourself, Ed," said the customer.

"Thanks, I'll take a cigar."

Eddie's waistcoat pockets, as day drew slowly on to evening, bristled with cigars like a fortress with cannon.

"Here, don't take a smoke, have a drink!" said the customer. "Thanks, I'll take a lemon sour. Here's luck." Lemon sours, sarsaparillas, and sickly beverages taken in little glassfuls, till the glassfuls ran into gallons—these were the price that Eddie paid for his abstemiousness.

"Don't you ever take anything, Ed?" asked the uninitiated. "I never use it," he answered.

. . . . . . .

But Eddie's principal office was that of a receptive listener, and, as such, always in agreement.

"Cold, ain't it?" said the customer.

"It sure is!" answered Eddie with a shiver.

"By Gosh, it's warm!" said another ten minutes later.

"Certainly a hot day," Ed murmured, quite faint with the heat.

. . . . . . .

Out of such gentle agreement is fabricated the structure of companionship.

"I'll bet you that John L. will lick Jim Corbett in one round!"

"I wouldn't be surprised," says Eddie.

"I'll bet you that this young Jim Corbett will trim John L. in five minutes!"

"Yes, I guess he might easily enough," says Eddie.

. . . . . . .

Out of this followed directly and naturally Eddie's function as arbitrator, umpire, and world's court.

"I'll leave it to Ed," calls the customer. "See here, Ed, didn't Maud S. hold the record at 2.35 before ever Jay Eye See ran at all? Ain't that so? I bet him a dollar and I says, 'I'll leave it to Ed,' says I."

That was the kind of question that Eddie had to arbitrate—technical, recondite, controversial. The chief editor of the Encyclopædia Britannica couldn't have touched it. And he had to do it with peace and good will on both sides, and make it end somehow with the interrogation, "What are you having, gentlemen?"

. . . . . . .

But Eddie was not only by profession a conversationalist, a companion, and a convivialist, he was also in his degree a medical man, prescribing for his patients.

This was chiefly in the busy early morning, when the bar first opened up for the day.

Eddie's "patients" lined up before him, asking for eye-openers, brain-clearers, head-removers.

Behind Eddie, on little shelves, was a regular pharma-copœia; a phalanx of bottles—ticketed, labelled—some with marbles in the top stopper, some with little squirting tubes in the mouth. Out of these came bitters, sweets, flavours, peppers—things that would open the eyes, lift the hair, and renovate the whole man.

Eddie, shaking and mixing furiously, proceeded to open their eyes, clear up their brains, and remove their heads.

"I've got a head this morning, Ed. Fix me up something to take it away."

"Sure," said Eddie in return, "I'll fix it for you."

. . . . . . .

By eight A.M. Eddie had them all straightened up and fixed. Some were even able to take a drink and start over.

. . . . . . .

This was in the early morning. But at other times, as for example, quite late at night, Ed appeared in another rôle—that of the champion strong man. Who would suspect the muscles of steel concealed behind Eddie's wicker cuffs and his soft white shirt-sleeves? Who could expect anger from a countenance so undisturbed, a nature so unruffled, a mind so little given to argument?

But wait! Listen to that fierce quarrel punctuated with unpunctuable language between two "bums" out on the barroom floor. Lo! at the height of it Eddie clears the mahogany counter in a single leap, seizes the two "bums" each by the collar, and with a short rush and a flying throw hurls them both out of the swinging doors bang on the sidewalk!

Anger? No, not that; inspired indignation is the proper phrase. Ed represented the insulted majesty of a peaceful public anxious only to be let alone.

"Don't make no trouble in here," was Eddie's phrase. There must be "no trouble" within the sacred precincts. Trouble was for the outside, for the sidewalk, for the open street, where "trouble" could lie breathing heavily in the gutter till a "cop" took it where it belonged.

Thus did Eddie, and his like, hurl "trouble" out into the street, and with it, had they only known it, hurled away their profession and their livelihood.

This was their downfall.

.    .    .    .    .    .    .

Thus on the sunshine of Eddie's tranquil life descended, shadow by shadow, the eclipse of prohibition.

Eddie watched its approach, nearer and nearer.

"What are you going to go at, Ed?" they asked.

"I've been thinking of going into chicken farming," Eddie used to answer, as he swabbed off the bar. "They say there's good money in chickens."

Next week it was turkeys.

"A fellow was in here telling me about it," Ed said. "They say there's big money in turkeys."

After that it was a farm in Vermont, and then it was a ranch out in Kansas. But it was always something agricultural, bucolic, quiet.

Meanwhile Eddie stayed right there, pumping up the flooding beer and swabbing off the foam from the mahogany, till the days, the hours, and the minutes ticked out his livelihood.

Like the boy on the burning deck, he never left.

.    .    .    .    .    .    .

Where is he now? Eddie and all the other Eddies, the thousands of them? I don't know. There are different theories about them. Some people say they turned into divinity students and that they are out as canvassers selling Bibles to the farmers. You may still recognize them, it is claimed, by the gentle way in which they say, "What's yours this morning?"

There is no doubt their tranquil existence, sheltered behind the tall mahogany, unfitted them for the rough and tumble of ordinary life.

Perhaps, under prohibition, they took to drink. In the cities, even their habitat has gone. The corner saloon is now a soda fountain, where golden-headed blondes ladle out red and white sundaes and mushy chocolates and smash eggs into orange phosphates.

But out in the solitude of the country you may still see, here and there, boarded up in oblivion and obliquity, the frame building that was once the "tavern." No doubt at night, if it's late enough and dark enough, ghostly voices still whisper in the empty barroom, haunted by the spectres of the Eddies—"What's yours, gentlemen?"

# The Perfect Salesman

I ADMIT at the outset that I know nothing direct, personal or immediate about business. I have never been in it. If I were told tomorrow to go out and make $100,000 I should scarcely know how to do it. If anybody showed me a man on the street and told me to sell him a municipal six per cent bond I shouldn't know how to begin: I wouldn't know how to "approach" him, or how to hold his interest, or how to make him forget his troubles, or how to clinch him, or strike him to the earth at the final moment.

As to borrowing money,—which is one of the great essentials of business,—I simply couldn't do it. As soon as I got across the steps of the bank I should get afraid,—scared that they would throw me out. I know, of course, from reading about it that this is mere silliness, that the bankers are there simply waiting to lend money,—just crazy to lend it. All you have to do is to invite the general manager out to lunch and tell him that you want half a million dollars to float a big proposition (you don't tell him what it is,—you just say that you'll let him know later) and the manager, so I gather, will be simply wild to lend you the money. All this I pick up from the conversations which I overhear at my club from men who float things. But I couldn't do it myself: there's an art in it: to borrow money, big money, you have to wear your clothes in a certain way, walk in a certain way, and have about you an air of solemnity and majesty,—something like the atmosphere of a Gothic cathedral. Small men like me and you, my dear reader, especially you, can't do it. We feel mean about it: and when we get the money, even if it is only ten dollars, we give ourselves away at once by wanting to hustle away with it too fast. The really big man in this kind of thing can borrow half a million, button it up in his chest, and then draw on his gloves and talk easily about the prospect of rain. I admit I couldn't do it. If I ever got that half a million dollars, I'd beat it out of the bank as fast as a cat going over a fence.

So, as I say, I make no pretensions to being a business man or to knowing anything about business. But I have a huge admiration for it, especially for big business, for the men at the top. They say that the whole railway business of this continent centres really in four men; and they say, too, that the whole money power of New York is really held by about six men; the entire forests of this country are practically owned by three men; the whole of South America, though it doesn't know it, is controlled by less than five men; and the Atlantic Ocean is now to all intents and purposes in the hands of a little international group of not more than seven and less than eight.

Think what it would mean to be one of those eight, or one of that four, or even, one or two of that three! There must be a tremendous fascination about it, to be in this kind of really Big Business: to sit at a desk and feel one's great brain slowly revolving on its axis; to know that one's capacious mind was majestically turning round and round, and to observe one's ponderous intellect moving irresistibly up and down.

We cannot wonder, when we reflect on this, that all the world nowadays is drawn by the fascination of business. It is not the money that people want: I will acquit humanity of that: few people care for money for its own sake: it is the thought of what can be done with the money.

"Oh, if I only had a million dollars!" I heard a woman say the other day on the platform of a social service meeting. And I could guess just what she meant,—that she would quit work and go to the South Sea Islands and play mah jong and smoke opium. I've had the same idea again and again.

## Salesmanship and the Perfect Salesman

The most essential feature of modern business is, I imagine, salesmanship. My readers may not appreciate this at once,—they seldom seem to get anything readily,— and so I will explain some of the reasons which lead me to think so. Without salesmanship we could not sell anything. If we could not sell anything we might as well not make anything, because if we made things and couldn't sell them it would be as bad as if we sold things and couldn't make them.

Hence the most terrible danger that the world can face is that everybody will be buying things and nobody able to sell them. This danger of not selling anything, which used to threaten the world with disaster only a short time ago, is now being removed. Salesmanship, my readers will be glad to learn,—at least, if the miserable creatures ever get thrilled at anything,—is being reduced to a science. A great number of Manuals of Salesmanship are now being placed within reach of everybody and from these we can gather the essentials of the subject.

In the small space which it is here feasible to devote to the subject it is not possible to treat in an adequate way such a vast and important subject as modern salesmanship. For complete information recourse should be had to any one of the many manuals to which I refer and which can be had at a trifling sum, such as ten dollars, or even more.

But we may indicate here a few of the principal points of salesmanship.

### Personality of the Salesman

It is essential that the salesman should have charm. If he wishes to sell anything,—let us say lead pipe for use in sewers and house drains,—he will find that what he needs most in selling is personal charm, a sort of indefinable manner, with just that little touch of noblesse which suggests the easy camaraderie of the menagerie. In other words, he must diffuse wherever he goes, in selling sewer pipes, a sense of sunshine which makes the world seem a little brighter when he is gone.

In person the perfect salesman should be rather tall with a figure which suggests, to his customers, the outline of the Venus de Milo. According to the Manuals of Salesmanship he can get this figure by taking exercises every morning on the floor of his hotel bedroom. But the discussion of that point has been undertaken already. Let us suppose him then with the characteristic figure of a Venus de Milo, or if one will of a Paduan Mercury, or of a Bologna sausage. We come, in any case, to the all important points of dress.

### How Shall the Perfect Salesman Dress?

Every manual on the subject emphasizes the large importance of dress for the salesman. Indeed there is probably nothing which has a greater bearing on success and failure in the salesman than his dress. The well dressed man,—in selling, let us say, municipal bonds, has an initial advantage over the man who comes into his customer's store in tattered rags, with his toes protruding from his boots, unshaved and with a general air of want and misery stamped all over him. Customers are quick to notice these little things. But let the salesman turn up in an appropriate costume, bright and neat from head to foot and bringing with him something of the gladness of the early spring and the singing bird and the customer is immediately impressed in his favour.

One asks, what then should be the costume of the perfect salesman? It is not an easy question to answer. Obviously his costume must vary with the season and with the weather and with the time of day. One might suggest, however, that on rising in the morning the salesman should throw round him a light peignoir of yellow silk or a figured kimono slashed from the hips with pink insertions and brought round in a bold sweep to the small of the back. This should be worn during the morning toilet while putting the hair up in its combs, while adjusting the dickie and easing the suspenders. If breakfast is taken in the bedroom the liver and bacon may be eaten in this costume.

Breakfast over, the great moment approaches for the perfect salesman to get out upon the street. Here the daintiest care must be selected in choosing his dress. And here we may interpose at once a piece of plain and vigorous advice:—the simplest is the best. The salesman makes a great mistake who comes into his customer's premises covered with jewellery, with earrings in his ears and expensive bracelets on his feet and ankles. Nor should there be in the salesman's dress anything the least suggestive of immodesty. No salesman should ever appear with bare arms, or with his waistcoat cut so low as to suggest impropriety. Some salesmen, especially in the hardware business, are tempted to appear with bare arms, but they ought not to do it. For evening wear and for social recreation the case is different.  When work is over the salesman in returning to his hotel may very properly throw on a georgette camisole open at the throat or a lace fichu with ear-flaps of perforated celluloid.  But the salesman should remember that for the hours of business anything in the way of a luxurious or suggestive costume should be avoided.  Unfortunately this is not always done.  I have myself again and again noticed salesmen, especially in the hardware business where they take their coats off, to be wearing a suit calculated to reveal their figure round the hips and the lower part of the back in an immodest way.

All this kind of thing should be avoided.  The salesman should select from his wardrobe (or from his straw valise) a suit of plain severe design, attractive and yet simple, good and yet bad, long and at the same time short, in other words, something that is expensive but cheap.

He should button this up in some simple way with just a plain clasp at the throat, agate perhaps or onyx, and then, having buttoned up all his buttons, but, mark me, not until then, he should go out upon the street prepared to do business.

Let any of my readers who doubts the importance of dress,—and some of them are nuts enough to doubt anything,—consider the following little anecdote of salesmanship.  It is one that I selected from among the many little anecdotes of the sort which are always inserted in the manuals.

### Anecdote of the Ill-Dressed Salesman

"A salesman in the middle west, whom we will call Mr. Blank, called upon a merchant, whom we will Mr. Nut, and finding no difficulty in approaching him started in to show him his line with every hope of selling him.  It should be explained that the line which Mr. Blank carried consisted of haberdashery, gents furnishings and cut-to-fit suits. Mr. Nut was evidently delighted with the samples and already a big pile of neckties, gents collarings, gents shirtings and gents sockings was stacked up on the counter and an order form for $375.50 all ready to sign, when Mr. Nut noticed the salesman's own costume. Mr. Blank, who was a careless man in regard to dress though otherwise a man of intelligence, was wearing a low crowned Derby hat with a scooping brim over his ears, a celluloid collar and a dickie that was too small for him. His coat sleeves came only a little way below his elbows and plainly showed his cuffs, fastened with long steel clips to his undershirt. In other words, the man somehow lacked *class*. Mr. Nut put down his pen. 'I'm sorry, Mr. Blank,' he said, 'I can't buy from you. Your line is all right but you lack something, I can't just say what, but if I had to give it a name I should call it *tone*.' Blank, however, who was a man of resource, at once realized his error. 'One moment, Mr. Nut,' he said, 'don't refuse this order too soon.' With that he gathered up his valise and his samples and retreated to the back of the store behind a screen. In a few minutes he reappeared *dressed in his own samples*. The merchant, delighted in the change in Mr. Blank's appearance, kissed him and signed the order."

## Approaching the Prospect

So much for the salesman's dress, a matter of great importance but still only a preliminary to our discussion. Let us suppose then our salesman, fully dressed, his buttons all adjusted and drawing well, his suspenders regulated and his dickie set well in place. His next task is to "approach" his customer.

All those who understand salesmanship are well aware this is the really vital matter. Everything depends on it. And nevertheless "approaching" the merchant is a thing of great difficulty. The merchant, if we may believe our best books on salesmanship, is as wary as a mountain antelope. At the least alarm he will leap from his counter ten feet in the air and rush to the top of his attic floor: or perhaps he will make a dive into his cellar where he will burrow his way among barrels and boxes and become completely hidden. In such a case he can only be dug out with a spade. Some merchants are even crafty enough to have an assistant or sentinel posted in such a way as to give the alarm of the salesman's approach.

How then can the salesman manage to get his interview with the merchant or, to use a technical term, to get next to his *prospect*? The answer is that he must "stalk" his prospect as the hunter stalks the mountain goat or the wild hog. Dressed in a becoming way he must circulate outside his prospect's premises, occasionally taking a peep at him through the window and perhaps imitating the song of a bird or the gentle cooing of a dove. Pleased with the soft note of the bird's song the prospect will presently be seen to relax into a smile. Now is the moment for the salesman to act. He enters the place boldly and says with a winning frankness, "Mr. Nut, you thought it was a bird. It was not. It was I. I am here to show you my line."

If the salesman has chosen his moment rightly he will win. The merchant, once decoyed into looking at the line, is easily landed. On the other hand, the prospect may refuse even now to see the salesman and the attack must begin again. This difficulty of getting the merchant to see the salesman even when close beside him and the way in which it can be overcome by perseverance is well illustrated by a striking little anecdote which I quote from a recent book on salesmanship. The work, I may say, is authoritative, having been written by a man with over thirty years of experience in selling hardware and perfumes in the middle southwest.

### Anecdote of the Invisible Merchant

"A salesman whom we will call Mr. M."—I should perhaps explain here the M. is not really his name but just an ingenious way of indicating him,—"while travelling in the interests of perfume in the middle southwest came to a town which we designate T. where he was most anxious to see a prospect whom we will speak of as P. Entering P.'s premises one morning M. asked if he could see P. P. refused. M. went out of the store and waited at the door until P. emerged at the noon hour. As soon as P. emerged M. politely asked if he could see him. P. refused to be seen. M. waited till night and then presented himself at P.'s residence. 'Mr. P.,' said M., 'can I see you?' 'No,' said P., 'you can't.' This sort of thing went on for several days, during which M. presented himself continually before P. who as continually refused to see him. M. was almost in despair,—"

Perhaps I may interrupt this little story a moment to beg my readers not to be too much oppressed by M.'s despair. In these anecdotes the salesmen are always in despair at the lowest point of the story. But it is only a sign that the clouds are breaking. I will beg my readers then,—if the poor simps have been getting depressed,—to cheer up and hear what follows:—

"M., we say, was almost in despair when an idea occurred to him. He knew that Mr. P. was a very religious man and always attended divine worship (church) every

Sunday.   Disguising himself, therefore, to look like one of
the apostles, M. seated himself at one side of Mr. P.'s pew.
Mr. P. mistaking him for St. Matthew, was easily induced,
during the sermon, to look over M.'s line of perfume."
The above anecdote incidentally raises the important
question how frank should the salesman be with his prospect.   Should he go to the length of telling the truth?
An answer to this is that frankness will be found to be
the best policy.   We will illustrate it with a little story
taken from the experience of a young salesman travelling
in the north southwest in the interest of brushes, face
powder and toilet notions.

### Anecdote of the Truthful Salesman

"A young salesman, whom he will indicate as Mr. As-
terisk, travelling 'in' brushes and toilet supplies, was one
day showing his line to Mr. Stroke, a drug merchant of a
town in the east north southwest.   Picking up one of the
sample brushes, Mr. S. said to the salesman, 'That's an excellent brush.'   Mr. A. answered, 'No, I'm sorry to say it
is not.   Its bristles fall out easily and the wood is not really
rosewood but a cheap imitation.'   Mr. S. was so pleased
with the young man's candour that he said, 'Mr. A. it is
not often I meet a salesman as candid as you are.   If you
will show me the rest of your line I shall be delighted to
fill out a first class order.'   'Mr. S.,' answered Mr. A., 'I'm
sorry to say that the whole line is as rotten as that brush.'
More delighted than ever Mr. S., who was a widower,
invited Mr. A. to his house where he met Mr. S.'s grown-
up daughter who kept house for him.   The two young
people immediately fell in love and were married, Mr. A.
moving into the house and taking over the business while
Mr. S., now without a home, went out selling brushes."

While we are speaking of the approach of the prospect it may be well to remind our readers very clearly,—for the poor guys don't seem to get anything unless we make it clear,—that a prospect otherwise invisible may be approached and seen by utilizing his fondness for amusements or sport. Many a man who is adamant at his place of business is mud on a golf course. The sternest and hardest of merchants may turn out to be an enthusiastic angler, or even a fisherman. The salesman who takes care to saunter into the store with a dead catfish in his pocket will meet with a cordial reception; and a conversation pleasantly initiated over the catfish and its habits may end in a handsome order. At other times it is even possible to follow the prospect out to his golf course or to track him out to the trout streams and round him up in the woods. In this case salesmanship takes on a close analogy with out-of-door hunting, the search for the prospect, the stalking of the prospect and the final encounter being very similar to accounts of the stalking of big game.

I append here an illustrative anecdote. As a matter of fact it was written not in reference to salesmanship but as an account of hunting the Wallaboo or Great Hog in the uplands of East Africa. But anybody familiar with stories of salesmanship will see at once that it fits both cases. I have merely altered the wording a little just at the end.

## Anecdote of a Hog

"I had been credibly informed," says the writer, "that there was at least a sporting chance of getting in touch with the Great Hog at his drinking time,—"

It will be observed that, apart from the capital letters, this is almost exactly the remark that a salesman often makes.

"The natives of the place told me that the Hog could probably be found soon after daylight at a stream about ten miles away where the brute was accustomed to drink and to catch fish. I, therefore, rose early, rode through the thick squab which covered the upland and reached the stream, or nullah, just after daybreak. There I concealed myself in a thick gob of fuz.

"I had not long to wait. The Great Hog soon appeared sniffing the air and snorting at the prospect of a drink. Extending himself prone on the bank with his snout in the water and his huge hind-quarters in the air, the Hog presented an ideal mark for the sportsman. I rose from my thicket, rifle in hand, and said, 'Mr. A. I have followed you out to this trout stream in the hope of getting a chance to show you my line. If you have a few minutes at your disposal I shall be glad to show you some samples. If you don't care to buy anything, I can assure you that it will be a pleasure to show my line.' "

The text seems to go a little wrong here but we can make it all right by reverting to the original which says,—

"After letting him have it thus I had no trouble in hauling the Great Hog up the bank, where I skinned him."

Just one other question may be mentioned before we pass on from this fascinating topic of salesmanship. Should a salesman accept presents, especially presents from ladies? On the whole we think not. It is a delicate problem and one which every young salesman must think out for himself. But the salesman should always remember that a firm refusal if made in a gracious and winning manner is not calculated to give offence. If after concluding his business the salesman finds that the merchant endeavours to slip a bracelet or a pair of earrings into his hand, the salesman should say, "I can't take it, old top, I really can't," then kiss the merchant on the forehead and withdraw.

A present from a lady should be returned with a neat little note so framed as to avoid all offence and yet letting the donor realize clearly that the salesman is not that kind of man.

# Homer and Humbug, an Academic Discussion

THE following discussion is of course only of interest to scholars. But, as the public schools returns show that in the United States there are now over a million coloured scholars alone, the appeal is wide enough.

I do not mind confessing that for a long time past I have been very sceptical about the classics. I was myself trained as a classical scholar. It seemed the only thing to do with me. I acquired such a singular facility in handling Latin and Greek that I could take a page of either of them, distinguish which it was by merely glancing at it, and, with the help of a dictionary and a pair of compasses, whip off a translation of it in less than three hours.

But I never got any pleasure from it. I lied about it. At first, perhaps, I lied through vanity. Any coloured scholar will understand the feeling. Later on I lied through habit; later still because, after all, the classics were all that I had and so I valued them. I have seen thus a deceived dog value a pup with a broken leg, and a pauper child nurse a dead doll with the sawdust out of it. So I nursed my dead Homer and my broken Demosthenes though I knew in my heart that there was more sawdust in the stomach of one modern author than in the whole lot of them. Observe, I am not saying which it is that has it full of it.

So, as I say, I began to lie about the classics. I said to people who knew no Greek that there was a sublimity, a majesty about Homer which they could never hope to

95

grasp. I said it was like the sound of the sea beating against the granite cliffs of the Ionian Esophagus: or words to that effect. As for the truth of it, I might as well have said that it was like the sound of a rum distillery running a night shift on half time. At any rate this is what I said about Homer, and when I spoke of Pindar,—the dainty grace of his strophes,—and Aristophanes, the delicious sallies of his wit, sally after sally, each sally explained in a note calling it a sally—I managed to suffuse my face with an animation which made it almost beautiful.

I admitted of course that Virgil in spite of his genius had a hardness and a cold glitter which resembled rather the brilliance of a cut diamond than the soft grace of a flower. Certainly I admitted this: the mere admission of it would knock the breath out of anyone who was arguing.

From such talks my friends went away sad. The conclusion was too cruel. It had all the cold logic of a syllogism (like that almost brutal form of argument so much admired in the Paraphernalia of Socrates). For if:—

Virgil and Homer and Pindar had all this grace, and pith
    and these sallies,—
And if I read Virgil and Homer and Pindar,
And if they only read Mrs. Wharton and Mrs. Humphrey
    Ward
Then where were they?

So continued lying brought its own reward in the sense of superiority and I lied more.

When I reflect that I have openly expressed regret, as a personal matter, even in the presence of women, for the missing books of Tacitus, and the entire loss of the Abracadabra of Polyphemus of Syracuse, I can find no words in which to beg for pardon. In reality I was just as much

worried over the loss of the ichthyosaurus. More, indeed:
I'd like to have seen it: but if the books Tacitus lost were
like those he didn't, I wouldn't.

I believe all scholars lie like this. An ancient friend
of mine, a clergyman, tells me that in Hesiod he finds a
peculiar grace that he doesn't find elsewhere. He's a liar.
That's all. Another man, in politics and in the legislature, tells me that every night before going to bed he reads
over a page or two of Thucydides to keep his mind fresh.
Either he never goes to bed or he's a liar. Doubly so: no
one could read Greek at that frantic rate: and anyway
his mind isn't fresh. How could it be, he's in the legislature. I don't object to this man talking freely of the
classics, but he ought to keep it for the voters. My own
opinion is that before he goes to bed he takes whiskey:
why call it Thucydides?

I know there are solid arguments advanced in favour of
the classics. I often hear them from my colleagues. My
friend the professor of Greek tells me that he truly believes
the classics have made him what he is. This is a very
grave statement, if well founded. Indeed I have heard
the same argument from a great many Latin and Greek
scholars. They all claim, with some heat, that Latin and
Greek have practically made them what they are. This
damaging charge against the classics should not be too
readily accepted. In my opinion some of these men would
have been what they are, no matter what they were.

Be this as it may, I for my part bitterly regret the lies
I have told about my appreciation of Latin and Greek
literature. I am anxious to do what I can to set things
right. I am therefore engaged on, indeed have nearly
completed, a work which will enable all readers to judge
the matter for themselves. What I have done is a translation of all the great classics, not in the usual literal way

but on a design that brings them into harmony with modern life. I will explain what I mean in a minute.

The translation is intended to be within reach of everybody. It is so designed that the entire set of volumes can go on a shelf twenty-seven feet long, or even longer. The first edition will be an *édition de luxe* bound in vellum, or perhaps in buckskin, and sold at five hundred dollars. It will be limited to five hundred copies and, of course, sold only to the feeble minded. The next edition will be the Literary Edition, sold to artists, authors, actors and contractors. After that will come the Boarding House Edition, bound in board and paid for in the same way.

My plan is to so transpose the classical writers as to give, not the literal translation word for word, but what is really the modern equivalent. Let me give an odd sample or two to show what I mean. Take the passage in the First Book of Homer that describes Ajax the Greek dashing into the battle in front of Troy. Here is the way it runs (as nearly as I remember), in the usual word for word translation of the classroom, as done by the very best professor, his spectacles glittering with the literary rapture of it.

"Then he too Ajax on the one hand leaped (or possibly jumped) into the fight wearing on the other hand, yes certainly a steel corselet (or possibly a bronze under tunic) and on his head of course, yes without doubt he had a helmet with a tossing plume taken from the mane (or perhaps extracted from the tail) of some horse which once fed along the banks of the Scamander (and it sees the herd and raises its head and paws the ground) and in his hand a shield worth a hundred oxen and on his knees too especially in particular greaves made by some cunning artificer (or perhaps blacksmith) and he blows the fire and it is hot. Thus Ajax leapt (or, better, was propelled from behind), into the fight."

Now that's grand stuff. There is no doubt of it. There's a wonderful movement and force to it. You can almost see it move, it goes so fast. But the modern reader can't get it. It won't mean to him what it meant to the early Greek. The setting, the costume, the scene has all got to be changed in order to let the reader have a real equivalent to judge just how good the Greek verse is. In my translation I alter it just a little, not much but just enough to give the passage a form that reproduces the proper literary value of the verses, without losing anything of the majesty. It describes, I may say, the Directors of the American Industrial Stocks rushing into the Balkan War Cloud.—

Then there came rushing to the shock of war
Mr. McNicoll of the C. P. R.
He wore suspenders and about his throat
High rose the collar of a sealskin coat.
He had on gaiters and he wore a tie,
He had his trousers buttoned good and high;
About his waist a woollen undervest
Bought from a sad-eyed farmer of the West.
(And every time he clips a sheep he sees
Some bloated plutocrat who ought to freeze),
Thus in the Stock Exchange he burst to view,
Leaped to the post, and shouted, "Ninety-two!"

There! That's Homer, the real thing! Just as it sounded to the rude crowd of Greek peasants who sat in a ring and guffawed at the rhymes and watched the minstrel stamp it out into "feet" as he recited it!

Or let me take another example from the so-called Catalogue of the Ships that fills up nearly an entire book of Homer. This famous passage names all the ships, one by one, and names the chiefs who sailed on them, and names the particular town or hill or valley that they came from.

It has been much admired. It has that same majesty of style that has been brought to an even loftier pitch in the New York Business Directory and the City Telephone Book. It runs along, as I recall it, something like this,—

"And first, indeed, oh yes, was the ship of Homistogetes the Spartan, long and swift, having both its masts covered with cowhide and two rows of oars. And he, Homistogetes, was born of Hermogenes and Ophthalmia and was at home in Syncope beside the fast flowing Paresis. And after him came the ship of Preposterus the Eurasian, son of Oasis and Hyteria," . . . and so on endlessly.

Instead of this I substitute, with the permission of the New York Central Railway, the official catalogue of their locomotives taken almost word for word from the list compiled by their superintendent of works. I admit that he wrote in hot weather. Part of it runs:—

> Out in the yard and steaming in the sun
> Stands locomotive engine number forty-one;
> Seated beside the windows of the cab
> Are Pat McGaw and Peter James McNab.
> Pat comes from Troy and Peter from Cohoes,
> And when they pull the throttle off she goes;
> And as she vanishes there comes to view
> Steam locomotive engine number forty-two.
> Observe her mighty wheels, her easy roll,
> With William J. Macarthy in control.
> They say her engineer some time ago
> Lived on a farm outside of Buffalo
> Whereas his fireman, Henry Edward Foy,
> Attended School in Springfield, Illinois.
> Thus does the race of man decay or rot—
> Some men can hold their jobs and some can not.

Please observe that if Homer had actually written that last line it would have been quoted for a thousand years as one of the deepest sayings ever said. Orators would have rounded out their speeches with the majestic phrase, quoted in sonorous and unintelligible Greek verse, "some men can hold their jobs and some can not": essayists would have begun their most scholarly dissertations with the words,—"It has been finely said by Homer that (in Greek) 'some men can hold their jobs' ": and the clergy in mid-pathos of a funeral sermon would have raised their eyes aloft and echoed "Some men can not"!

This is what I should like to do. I'd like to take a large stone and write on it in very plain writing,—

"The classics are only primitive literature. They belong in the same class as primitive machinery and primitive music and primitive medicine,"—and then throw it through the windows of a University and hide behind a fence to see the professors buzz!!

# Back to the Bush

I HAVE a friend called Billy, who has the Bush Mania. By trade he is a doctor, but I do not think that he needs to sleep out of doors. In ordinary things his mind appears sound. Over the tops of his gold-rimmed spectacles, as he bends forward to speak to you, there gleams nothing but amiability and kindliness. Like all the rest of us he is, or was until he forgot it all, an extremely well-educated man.

I am aware of no criminal strain in his blood. Yet Billy is in reality hopelessly unbalanced. He has the Mania of the Open Woods.

Worse than that, he is haunted with the desire to drag his friends with him into the depths of the Bush.

Whenever we meet he starts to talk about it.

Not long ago I met him in the club.

"I wish," he said, "you'd let me take you clear away up the Gatineau."

"Yes, I wish I would, I don't think," I murmured to myself, but I humoured him and said:

"How do we go, Billy, in a motor-car or by train?"

"No, we paddle."

"And is it up-stream all the way?"

"Oh, yes," Billy said enthusiastically.

"And how many days do we paddle all day to get up?"

"Six."

"Couldn't we do it in less?"

"Yes," Billy answered, feeling that I was entering into the spirit of the thing, "if we start each morning just before daylight and paddle hard till moonlight, we could do it in five days and a half."

"Glorious! and are there portages?"

"Lots of them."

"And at each of these do I carry two hundred pounds of stuff up a hill on my back?"

"Yes."

"And will there be a guide, a genuine, dirty-looking Indian guide?"

"Yes."

"And can I sleep next to him?"

"Oh, yes, if you want to."

"And when we get to the top, what is there?"

"Well, we go over the height of land."

"Oh, we do, do we?  And is the height of land all rock and about three hundred yards up-hill?  And do I carry a barrel of flour up it?  And does it roll down and crush me on the other side?  Look here, Billy, this trip is a great thing, but it is too luxurious for me.  If you will have me paddled up the river in a large iron canoe with an awning, carried over the portages in a sedan-chair, taken across the height of land in a palanquin or a howdah, and lowered down the other side in a derrick, I'll go. Short of that, the thing would be too fattening."

Billy was discouraged and left me.  But he has since returned repeatedly to the attack.

He offers to take me to the head-waters of the Batiscan. I am content at the foot.

He wants us to go to the sources of the Attahwapiscat. I don't.

He says I ought to see the grand chutes of the Kewakasis.  Why should I?

I have made Billy a counter-proposition that we strike through the Adirondacks (in the train) to New York, from there portage to Atlantic City, then to Washington, carrying our own grub (in the dining-car), camp there a few days (at the Willard), and then back, I to return by train and Billy on foot with the outfit.

The thing is still unsettled.

Billy, of course, is only one of thousands that have got this mania. And the autumn is the time when it rages at its worst.

Every day there move northward trains, packed full of lawyers, bankers, and brokers, headed for the bush. They are dressed up to look like pirates. They wear slouch hats, flannel shirts, and leather breeches with belts. They could afford much better clothes than these, but they won't use them. I don't know where they get these clothes. I think the railroad lends them out. They have guns between their knees and big knives at their hips. They smoke the worst tobacco they can find, and they carry ten gallons of alcohol per man in the baggage car.

In the intervals of telling lies to one another they read the railroad pamphlets about hunting. This kind of literature is deliberately and fiendishly contrived to infuriate their mania. I know all about these pamphlets because I write them. I once, for instance, wrote up, from imagination, a little place called Dog Lake at the end of a branch line. The place had failed as a settlement, and the railroad had decided to turn it into a hunting resort. I did the turning. I think I did it rather well, rechristening the lake and stocking the place with suitable varieties of game. The pamphlet ran like this.

"The limpid waters of Lake Owatawetness (the name, according to the old Indian legends of the place, signifies, The Mirror of the Almighty) abound with every known variety of fish. Near to its surface, so close that the angler may reach out his hand and stroke them, schools of pike,

pickerel, mackerel, doggerel, and chickerel jostle one another in the water.   They rise instantaneously to the bait
and swim gratefully ashore holding it in their mouths.   In
the middle depth of the waters of the lake, the sardine, the
lobster, the kippered herring, the anchovy and other tinned
varieties of fish disport themselves with evident gratifica-
tion, while even lower in the pellucid depths the dog-fish,
the hog-fish, the log-fish, and the sword-fish whirl about
in never-ending circles.

"Nor is Lake Owatawetness merely an Angler's Paradise.
Vast forests of primeval pine slope to the very shores of
the lake, to which descend great droves of bears—brown,
green, and bear-coloured—while as the shades of evening
fall, the air is loud with the lowing of moose, cariboo,
antelope, cantelope, musk-oxes, musk-rats, and other gra-
minivorous mammalia of the forest.   These enormous
quadrumana generally move off about 10.30 p.m., from
which hour until 11.45 p.m. the whole shore is reserved
for bison and buffalo.

"After midnight hunters who so desire it can be chased
through the woods, for any distance and at any speed they
select, by jaguars, panthers, cougars, tigers, and jackals
whose ferocity is reputed to be such that they will tear
the breeches off a man with their teeth in their eagerness
to sink their fangs in his palpitating flesh.   Hunters, attention!   Do not miss such attractions as these!"

I have seen men—quiet, reputable, well-shaved men—
reading that pamphlet of mine in the rotundas of hotels,
with their eyes blazing with excitement.   I think it is the
jaguar attraction that hits them the hardest, because I
notice them rub themselves sympathetically with their
hands while they read.

Of course, you can imagine the effect of this sort of

literature on the brains of men fresh from their offices, and dressed out as pirates.

They just go crazy and stay crazy.

Just watch them when they get into the bush.

Notice that well-to-do stockbroker crawling about on his stomach in the underbrush, with his spectacles shining like gig-lamps. What is he doing? He is after a cariboo that isn't there. He is "stalking" it. With his stomach. Of course, away down in his heart he knows that the cariboo isn't there and never was; but that man read my pamphlet and went crazy. He can't help it: he's *got* to stalk something. Mark him as he crawls along; see him crawl through a thimbleberry bush (very quietly so that the cariboo won't hear the noise of the prickles going into him), then through a bee's nest, gently and slowly, so that the cariboo will not take fright when the bees are stinging him. Sheer woodcraft! Yes, mark him. Mark him any way you like. Go up behind him and paint a blue cross on the seat of his pants as he crawls. He'll never notice. He thinks he's a hunting dog. Yet this is the man who laughs at his little son of ten for crawling round under the dining-room table with a mat over his shoulders, and pretending to be a bear.

Now see these other men in camp.

Someone has told them—I think I first started the idea in my pamphlet—that the thing is to sleep on a pile of hemlock branches. I think I told them to listen to the wind sowing (you know the word I mean), sowing and crooning in the giant pines. So there they are upside-down, doubled up on a couch of green spikes that would have killed St. Sebastian. They stare up at the sky with blood-shot, restless eyes, waiting for the crooning to begin. And there isn't a sow in sight.

Here is another man, ragged and with a six days' growth

of beard, frying a piece of bacon on a stick over a little fire.  Now what does he think he is?  The *chef* of the Waldorf Astoria?  Yes, he does, and what's more he thinks that that miserable bit of bacon, cut with a tobacco knife from a chunk of meat that lay six days in the rain, is fit to eat.  What's more, he'll eat it.  So will the rest.  They're all crazy together.

There's another man, the Lord help him, who thinks he has the "knack" of being a carpenter.  He is hammering up shelves to a tree.  Till the shelves fall down he thinks he is a wizard.  Yet this is the same man who swore at his wife for asking him to put up a shelf in the back kitchen.  "How the blazes," he asked, "could he nail the damn thing up?  Did she think he was a plumber?"

After all, never mind.

Provided they are happy up there, let them stay.

Personally, I wouldn't mind if they didn't come back and lie about it.  They get back to the city dead fagged for want of sleep, sogged with alcohol, bitten brown by the bush-flies, trampled on by the moose and chased through the brush by bears and skunks—and they have the nerve to say that they like it.

Sometimes I think they do.

Men are only animals anyway.  They like to get out into the woods and growl round at night and feel something bite them.

Only why haven't they the imagination to be able to do the same thing with less fuss?  Why not take their coats and collars off in the office and crawl round on the floor and growl at one another.  It would be just as good.

# The Doctor and the Contraption

## I

### MEDICINE AS IT WAS

I SUPPOSE that when an up-to-date doctor of today looks at you or me, or at any one of us, he sees something very different from what we see. In place of a human personality—a soul looking out from the infinite depth of the human eye—he sees a collection of tubes, feed-pipes, conduits, joints, levers, and food and water tanks. He sees thirty-five feet of internal elastic piping, a hundred and ten feet of wiring, together with a pound and a half of brain, arrayed behind a couple of optical lenses set in gimbals. In other words, what he sees is not a man at all but a complicated machine contraption, probably running very badly, wheezing in the pipes and clogged in the carburetor. Naturally he wants to get at it, just as a garage man longs to tear a motor to pieces. He would like to take a monkey-wrench and tighten up its joints; turn a hose into it and flush out its piping; or better still, put a new boiler into it and throw the old one away.

This is what is called the Medical Instinct. There is something fierce, as it were, to the verge of comicality in what a doctor would like to do to a patient short of driving shingle nails into him with a tack hammer. Even that might come in handy.

But contrast the change there has been in the common practice of medicine within a couple of generations. Compare the medicine of fifty years ago with the medicine of today and we can easily foresee the further progress of the science.

Thus, first:

## MEDICINE YEAR, 1880

### *The Saviour of Men*

In the old-fashioned days when a man got sick he went to a family doctor and said he was sick. The doctor gave him a bottle of medicine. He took it home and drank it and got well.

On the bottle was written, "Three times a day, in water." The man drank it three times a day the first day, twice the second day, and once the third day. On the fourth day he forgot it. But that didn't matter. He was well by that time.

The place where he visited the doctor was the doctor's own house, in the room called the "surgery" which was the same room as the one where they played euchre in the evening. There was no apparatus in it, except fishing rods and shotguns.

The doctor mixed the medicine himself at the tap over the sink. He put in anything that he had—it didn't matter much what. As a matter of fact the man began to feel better as soon as he saw the medicine being mixed.

The doctor didn't take an X-ray of the patient. He couldn't. There weren't any. He didn't test his blood pressure or examine his arteries; people had none then.

Very often after the patient had gone away the doctor, if he was a thoughtful man, would sit and smoke a pipe and wonder what was wrong with the man anyway. But he never, never expressed any such wonder or doubt to the man himself. His profession had learned this maxim from Hippocrates and it had come down as an unbroken tradition. The medical profession never talked medicine to the patient.

Sometimes the doctor suspected that the man was really ill. But he never said so. Only after the patient was quite well again, did the doctor tell him how ill he had been. Hence every illness appeared in retrospect as a close shave in which a timely dose of medicine had saved a human life. This raised the whole tone of the business. The doctor appeared as a saviour of men. As he got older his beard—all doctors wore beards—became tinged with grey; his person acquired an easy dignity; his expression, something of nobility. He cured the patient by his presence. Beyond that, all he needed was a bottle of medicine and a cork. In an extreme case, he sat beside the patient's bed in a long vigil that might last all night. But the patient was well in the morning.

For convalescence the doctor prescribed a "light diet." This meant beefsteak and porter.

.     .     .     .     .     .     .

Such medicine, of course, was hopelessly unscientific, hopelessly limited. Death could beat it round every corner. But it was human, gracious, kindly. Today it is replaced by "machine medicine" with the mechanical test, the scientific diagnosis, the hospital, the X-ray. All this is marvellous. But no one has yet combined it with the Art of Healing.

As witness:

## II

### MEDICINE YEAR, 1932

#### THE DOCTOR AND THE CONTRAPTION

The Contraption sits huddled up in its serge suit in a consultation office chair.  Its locomotive apparatus is doubled up beneath it, folded at the joints.  The thing is anxious, but the doctor doesn't know that.  The poor Contraption is consumed with something like panic that is gripping it by the feed-pipe.  But it makes as brave a show as it can.

"It's a little hard to say," says the doctor, "just what the trouble is."

He has been making a few preliminary investigations by punching and listening in.

"I don't know that I quite like that heart," he adds, and then relapses into a reflective silence.

"Yes," he continues, as he comes out of his reverie, "there are symptoms there that I don't like—don't like at all."

Neither does the Contraption, but he keeps quiet.

"There may be," says the doctor, "an ankylosis there."

What an ankylosis is and what it does, the Contraption doesn't know.  But the sound of it is quite enough.

"It's just possible," says the doctor as another bright idea occurs to him, "that there's an infiltration into the proscenium."

These may not be the exact medical terms that the doctor uses.  But that is what they sound like to the Contraption.

"Is that so?" he says.

"However, we'll keep that under observation till we

see what we find. You say you never had hydrophobia?"

"Not so far as I remember."

"That's interesting. The symptoms seem to suggest hydrophobia, or just possibly hendiadys."

The doctor reflects a little more, then he begins to write on little bits of paper.

"Well," he says in a cheerful tone, "we'll try it out anyway."

He writes out little orders for X-rays, blood tests, heart tests.

"Now," he says in conclusion. "Don't be alarmed. You may blow up on the street. But I don't think so. I'm not much afraid of that. It's possible that your brain will burst open at the sides. But I'm not alarmed if it does. If your eyes fall out on the street, let me know."

These are not his exact words. But they give exactly the impression that his words convey.

"I will," says the Contraption.

"And now," says the doctor, who by this time has warmed up to the case and is filled with artistic interest, "about diet—I think you'd better not eat anything—or not for a month or so; and don't drink; and you may as well cut out tobacco, and you'd better not sleep.

"And above all," concludes the doctor with a sudden burst of geniality that he had forgotten to use sooner, "don't worry. You may blow up at any time, but don't let that worry you. You may fall dead in a taxi, but I'm not alarmed if you do. Come back in a week and I'll show you the X-ray plates. Good-bye."

The Contraption goes away for a week. That means seven days, or 168 hours, or 10,080 minutes, or 604,800 seconds. And he knows every one of them. He feels them go by.

When he comes back in a week he finds the doctor beaming with interest.

"Look at them," he says, holding up to the light some photographic plates.

"What are those?" asks the Contraption.

"The brain," says the doctor. "You see that misty-looking spot—there, just between the encephalon and the encyclopædia—?"

"What is it?" asks the Contraption.

"I don't know yet," the doctor says. "It's a little early to say. But we'll watch it. If you don't mind, I think we'll probably open your head and take a look. They are doing some wonderful things now in the removal of the brain. It's rather a nice operation, but I think I may take the risk. I'll let you know. Meantime you're following out our instructions, I hope, not eating anything."

"Oh, no."

"And nothing to drink or smoke."

"Oh, no."

"That's right. Well, now, in a day or two we'll know more. I'll have your blood by that time and the sections of your heart and then I think we'll begin to see where we are. Good-bye."

. . . . . . .

A week or so later the doctor says to his lady secretary, "That Contraption in the serge suit, wasn't he to have come in this morning?"

The lady looked over a memorandum book. "Yes, I think he was."

"Well, call him up on the 'phone. He doesn't need to come. I've had all his hospital reports and they can't find anything wrong at all. Tell him they want him to come back in six months and they may find something then.

But there's absolutely nothing wrong with him now, unless it's his imagination. And, oh, by the way, tell him this—it will amuse him. That cloud on the X-ray plate that looked like a clot on the brain turns out to be a flaw in the glass. He'll have a good laugh at that."

The secretary vanishes into the telephone room and it is some little time before she comes back.

"Well?" says the doctor, "did you get that gentleman on the 'phone?" He calls him a gentleman now because medical interest in him is over.

"I got his house," she answers, "but they say the gentleman is dead. He died last night."

"Dear me!" says the doctor gravely. "So we were wrong after all; we should have tested for something else. Did they say anything about how he died?"

"Yes. They say that as far as they know he died from gas. He seems to have turned on gas in the bedroom on purpose."

"Tut, tut," says the doctor, "suicidal mania! I forgot to test him for it!"

### III

### THE WALRUS AND THE CARPENTER

But, still humanity gets used to anything and thrives on it. Already this new method of medicine, this tinkering, testing, inoculating, is a recognized part of our common life. Already we can see developing in it the healing art of the future; or rather, not the healing art which is a thing lost in the past and surviving only by the wayside. What is replacing it, is better called the art of reconstruction. Its aim is not to heal the patient; he's not worth it; reconstruct him; make him over. If his engine doesn't work, put a new one in him.  Everyone today knows in a general sort of way something of what is being done in reconstructive surgery.  Bones are taken out and new ones put in.  Patches of skin from Mr. Jones are grafted on to Mr. Smith.  No one cares to think out too completely the gruesome details or to ask where they are leading.  But the goal is plain enough.  And no doubt when it is reached all idea of gruesomeness will have vanished from it.  Ideas of that sort are only secondary and relative, things with no basis in absolute reality.  An octopus looks terrible; a cooked lobster looks delicious.  If no one had ever seen a cooked lobster, a whole supper party would rise, shrieking with terror at the sight of one.

Thus it would seem probable that with the triumphant progress of reconstructive surgery, all sense of terror or gruesomeness will pass away.  We are quite used to people with false teeth; we are getting used to people with lifted faces; and presently we shall not shrink in alarm from a friend who has just bought a brand new stomach:

In witness of which:

## MEDICINE YEAR, 2000

### The Walrus and the Carpenter

"Now, I'd like to have him pretty well made over from the start," said the self-assertive lady to the doctor.

As she said it she indicated a miserable-looking creature, evidently her husband, sitting flopped in a chair, gazing feebly at his wife and at the doctor.

The woman was of that voluble, obtrusive, assertive type that has made the two sexes what they are.

The man was of the familiar pattern of the henpecked husband, with a face as meek in expression as the countenance of a walrus, and with the ragged drooping moustache that belongs with it.

"Oh, I don't know about that," he murmured.

But neither the lady nor the doctor paid much attention to what he murmured.

"He needs nearly everything new," said the woman, "and I've been telling him I'm going to give it to him as a present for our wedding anniversary next month. It will be twenty-five years we've been married."

"Twenty-five years!" said the doctor.

"Of course," gurgled the lady. "I was just a mere girl when we got married. They used to call me the little Rose Bud!"

"Yes, yes," murmured the doctor. He was looking at the lady in an absent-minded way, not really seeing her. Perhaps he was thinking that no lapse of time, no passage of generations can alter this type of woman or vary this line of conversation. On the other hand, perhaps he wasn't. He may have been merely thinking of the case. It was not every day that Dr. Carpenter was called upon to do what was called in his profession "a complete job." To put in a new bone or two or insert part of a brain or to replace an old stomach was an everyday matter. But to make a subject over from head to toe was still unusual and perhaps a trifle experimental.

"As a matter of fact," the husband began again, "I'm not so sure that I really need so very much done; in fact so far as I am concerned—"

"Now, John," interposed his wife, "don't let me hear any more of that. This is my business and not yours. I'm going to pay for it all out of my own money, and you're not to say another word."

The doctor was looking meditatively at the patient. He

seemed to be measuring him with his eye. "There's a lot of him that I can use," he said.

"How do you mean?" asked the lady.

"Well, for instance, his head. That's all right. I can use his head as it is."

"Not his face!" said the lady.

"Yes, even his face, in a way. You'd be surprised what can be done without any radical replacement of tissue. What his face needs is not any change, but more animation, more expression, more alertness. You wait till I've put about twenty thousand volts of electricity through it, and see how it looks then."

"I say," murmured the man, "I'm not so sure that I feel so very keen about that."

"You won't know it," said the doctor tersely, and then continuing, "and I don't see why I couldn't use his framework. The arms and legs are all right."

The woman shook her head.

"He's not tall enough," she said.

"Personally," began the man, but his wife paid no attention to him and went on.

"He needs *presence*. He makes such a poor appearance when we go out evenings. I'd like him quite a lot taller."

"Very good," said Dr. Carpenter. "It's easily done. I can put in another six inches in the thigh bone simply enough. He'll look a little short when he sits at table but that won't matter so much. But of course to get the right proportion you'll need to alter the arms as well. By the way," he added as a new idea seemed to occur to him, "do you play golf?"

"Do I play?" said the patient, showing for the first time an obvious animation. "Do I do anything else? I play every day, and yet would you believe it, I'm about the worst player in the club. Take yesterday, for instance,

I'd come down the long hole, four hundred and eighty yards in three—right on to the green, and there I stuck—seven more to get into the hole. Seven! Can you beat it?"

"I'll tell you," said the doctor. "If you feel that way about it, I might do something about your golf while I am altering your arm."

"Say, if you could, I'd pay a thousand dollars for that," said the man. "Do you think you can?"

"Wait a bit," said the doctor. He stepped into the adjacent telephone cupboard. What he said and what was said to him was not audible to either Mr. Walrus or to his wife. The detailed operations of the medical profession are not either now or in Utopia as noble to contemplate as its final achievements. But if there had been an ear to listen when the dial was turned, this is what it would have heard.

"It's Dr. Carpenter. What about that Scotch professional golfer that you got yesterday? Is he all gone?"

"Wait a minute, doctor, I'll ask. . . . No, they say nothing much gone yet. Do you want his brain?"

The doctor laughed. "No, thanks. I want his right forearm. I've a client who'll pay anything that's fair up to a thousand. Right. Thank you."

"That'll be all right," said the doctor. "I can put a golf adjuster in you; and so now I think we can go right ahead, eh?"

"There's just one thing," said the wife, "that I'd like changed more than anything else. John is always so retiring and shy. He don't make the most of himself."

"Oh, come, come, June!" protested the man bluntly, "there's nothing in me to make much of."

"Well, I think," the woman went on, "that John's got what they call an 'inferiority complex.' Isn't that the word?   Now couldn't you do something to his brain to get that out of it?"

Dr. Carpenter smiled.

"That's not in his brain, Mrs. Walrus; that's a matter of his glands and there's nothing easier than to alter that. The adjustment is a little difficult, the only danger is that he may get a little the other way."

"That's all right," said the woman, "that won't hurt him.   He needs it."

.    .    .    .    .    .    .

It would be grossly out of place to linger on the details of the weeks of "treatment" which followed for Mr. Walrus.   Such things belong only in a book of technical medicine.   Even nowadays we prefer to leave all that in a half light, and in future generations, convention will dictate a still greater reticence in regard to the processes of reconstructive surgery.   In any case the use of *sustained* anæsthetics in place of the intermittent anæsthetics of today put a different complexion on the whole affair. Convalescence itself being under anæsthetics, the patient —or rather client, to use the more ordinary term—knows nothing from his entrance into the Refactorium (formerly called hospital) until his final exit.   The declaration of such a client that he "felt a new man" had a more literal meaning than now.

Suffice it to say that within a week or so Mrs. Walrus received a telephone communication from the hospital which said, "His legs are done."   A little after that came an inquiry, "How about his whiskers?   Would you like to preserve them or will you have a permanent clean shave?"

.    .    .    .    .    .    .

Under such circumstances, Dr. Carpenter was not at all surprised when in about six weeks from the original interview the renovated John Walrus walked into his office. He was all the less surprised because of the fact that Mr. Walrus was practically unrecognizable as his former self. What the doctor saw now was a tall man whose erect bearing was almost a perpendicular line and whose clean-shaven face, hard square jaw (evidently brand new) proclaimed a man of character and determination.

"Mr. Walrus!" exclaimed Dr. Carpenter when at last he realized who it was.

"I am," said the man, shaking hands with a cordial but firm clasp, "though it's a measly sort of name and I don't like it."

"And how do you feel?" asked the doctor.

"Fine," said Walrus. "I've just been out on the links. I went right up there first thing as soon as I came out. Do you know, I went round under forty; and that long hole I did in four—can you believe it?—one under the par. Certainly the rest and the treatment have done wonders for my arm."

"Certainly," repeated the doctor.

"Though as a matter of fact," Walrus continued, "I think I've a natural aptitude for the game. After all, you know, brain counts in golf as well as brawn. But, however, that's not what I came to talk about but just to thank you and to ask you to be good enough to have your account sent to me—to me personally, you understand."

"But I thought," said Dr. Carpenter, "that Mrs. Walrus wanted to pay it herself?"

"Nothing doing," laughed the client. "I'm not such a fool as that. If she paid it, it would create a sort of lien, don't you see, legally?"

"Oh, I know that," said the doctor. "The case often

occurs.   Still, in your instance I should have thought—"

"There's more to it than that," said Walrus, pausing to light a cigarette.   "I went up to the house and saw her. My heavens, Carpenter, what a tongue that woman has! Absolutely never stops!   The fact is, I don't think I care to go back to her.   She'd talk me to death."

"As far as that goes," said the doctor, "if it was only a matter of her tongue, I could shorten it for you."

"You could, eh?"   For a moment Mr. Walrus paused as if in some slight doubt.   Then he went on speaking in the firm decisive way that was now, since twenty-four hours, habitual with him.

"No, no, it's too late now.   And anyway, I don't want to.   The fact is, Carpenter, that I have arranged to take a new wife.   I've decided, in short, to take one of the nurses from up at the hospital.   You may have noticed her when you were up there, the dark, very tall one.   In fact, if anything, she's a little too tall."

"I could shorten her," murmured Carpenter.

"By how much?" asked Walrus—"Or no, I'll keep her as she is."

"And when do you get married?" asked the doctor.

"I haven't quite decided," replied Walrus.   "Very soon, I think."

"No doubt," said the doctor, "the young lady is equally keen on it?"

"I haven't asked her yet," said Walrus.   "I shall probably mention it to her today.   But I want to go and have another eighteen holes first.   Well, good-bye, doctor, don't forget the account, and by the way, when you make it out to me kindly alter the name.   After this I'm changing my name from John Walrus to Hercules Bullrush."

.        .        .                    .        .        .

After the client had gone out, Dr. Carpenter, who was a thoughtful man, sat down at his desk and continued his work upon his forthcoming treatise, "On the Probable Limitations of Restorative Surgery."

# The Awful Fate of Melpomenus Jones

SOME people—not you nor I, because we are so awfully self-possessed—but some people, find great difficulty in saying good-bye when making a call or spending the evening. As the moment draws near when the visitor feels that he is fairly entitled to go away he rises and says abruptly, "Well, I think I . . ." Then the people say, "Oh, must you go now? Surely it's early yet!" and a pitiful struggle ensues.

I think the saddest case of this kind of thing that I ever knew was that of my poor friend Melpomenus Jones, a curate—such a dear young man, and only twenty-three! He simply couldn't get away from people. He was too modest to tell a lie, and too religious to wish to appear rude. Now it happened that he went to call on some friends of his on the very first afternoon of his summer vacation. The next six weeks were entirely his own—absolutely nothing to do. He chatted awhile, drank two cups of tea, then braced himself for the effort and said suddenly:

"Well, I think I . . ."

But the lady of the house said, "Oh, no! Mr. Jones, can't you really stay a little longer?"

Jones was always truthful. "Oh, yes," he said, "of course, I—er—can stay."

"Then please don't go."

He stayed. He drank eleven cups of tea. Night was falling. He rose again.

"Well now," he said shyly, "I think I really . . ."

"You must go?" said the lady politely. "I thought perhaps you could have stayed to dinner . . ."

"Oh well, so I could, you know," Jones said, "if . . ."

"Then please stay, I'm sure my husband will be delighted."

"All right," he said feebly, "I'll stay," and he sank back into his chair, just full of tea, and miserable.

Papa came home. They had dinner. All through the meal Jones sat planning to leave at eight-thirty. All the family wondered whether Mr. Jones was stupid and sulky, or only stupid.

After dinner mamma undertook to "draw him out," and showed him photographs. She showed him all the family museum, several gross of them—photos of papa's uncle and his wife, and mamma's brother and his little boy, an awfully interesting photo of papa's uncle's friend in his Bengal uniform, an awfully well-taken photo of papa's grandfather's partner's dog, and an awfully wicked one of papa as the devil for a fancy-dress ball.

At eight-thirty Jones had examined seventy-one photographs. There were about sixty-nine more that he hadn't. Jones rose.

"I must say good night now," he pleaded.

"Say good night!" they said, "why it's only half-past eight! Have you anything to do?"

"Nothing," he admitted, and muttered something about staying six weeks, and then laughed miserably.

Just then it turned out that the favourite child of the family, such a dear little romp, had hidden Mr. Jones's hat; so papa said that he must stay, and invited him to a pipe and a chat. Papa had the pipe and gave Jones the chat, and still he stayed. Every moment he meant to take the plunge, but couldn't. Then papa began to get very tired of Jones, and fidgeted and finally said, with jocular irony, that Jones had better stay all night, they could give him a shake-down.    Jones mistook his meaning and thanked him with tears in his eyes, and papa put Jones to bed in the spare room and cursed him heartily.

After breakfast next day, papa went off to his work in the City, and left Jones playing with the baby, broken-hearted.    His nerve was utterly gone.    He was meaning to leave all day, but the thing had got on his mind and he simply couldn't.    When papa came home in the evening he was surprised and chagrined to find Jones still there. He thought to jockey him out with a jest, and said he thought he'd have to charge him for his board, he! he! The unhappy young man stared wildly for a moment, then wrung papa's hand, paid him a month's board in advance, and broke down and sobbed like a child.

In the days that followed he was moody and unap-proachable.    He lived, of course, entirely in the drawing-room, and the lack of air and exercise began to tell sadly on his health.    He passed his time in drinking tea and looking at the photographs.    He would stand for hours gazing at the photographs of papa's uncle's friend in his Bengal uniform—talking to it, sometimes swearing bit-terly at it.    His mind was visibly failing.

At length the crash came.    They carried him upstairs in a raging delirium of fever.    The illness that followed was terrible.    He recognised no one, not even papa's uncle's friend in his Bengal uniform.    At times he would start up from his bed and shriek, "Well, I think I . . ." and then fall back upon the pillow with a horrible laugh. Then, again, he would leap up and cry, "Another cup of tea and more photographs!    More photographs!    Har! Har!"

At length, after a month of agony, on the last day of his vacation, he passed away.    They say that when the last moment came, he sat up in bed with a beautiful smile of confidence playing upon his face, and said, "Well—the angels are calling me; I'm afraid I really must go now. Good afternoon."

And the rushing of his spirit from its prison-house was as rapid as a hunted cat passing over a garden fence.

# Number Fifty-Six

WHAT I narrate was told me one winter's evening by my friend Ah-Yen in the little room behind his laundry. Ah-Yen is a quiet little celestial with a grave and thoughtful face, and that melancholy contemplative disposition so often noticed in his countrymen. Between myself and Ah-Yen there exists a friendship of some years' standing, and we spend many a long evening in the dimly lighted room behind his shop, smoking a dreamy pipe together and plunged in silent meditation. I am chiefly attracted to my friend by the highly imaginative cast of his mind, which is, I believe, a trait of the Eastern character and which enables him to forget to a great extent the sordid cares of his calling in an inner life of his own creation. Of the keen, analytical side of his mind, I was in entire ignorance until the evening of which I write.

The room where we sat was small and dingy, with but little furniture except our chairs and the little table at which we filled and arranged our pipes, and was lighted only by a tallow candle. There were a few pictures on the walls, for the most part rude prints cut from the columns of the daily press and pasted up to hide the bareness of the room. Only one picture was in any way noticeable, a portrait admirably executed in pen and ink. The face was that of a young man, a very beautiful face, but one of infinite sadness. I had long been aware, although I know not how, that Ah-Yen had met with a great sorrow, and had in some way connected the fact with this portrait. I had always refrained, however, from asking him about it, and it was not until the evening in question that I knew its history.

We had been smoking in silence for some time when Ah-Yen spoke. My friend is a man of culture and wide reading, and his English is consequently perfect in its construction; his speech is, of course, marked by the lingering liquid accent of his country which I will not attempt to reproduce.

"I see," he said, "that you have been examining the portrait of my unhappy friend, Fifty-Six. I have never yet told you of my bereavement, but as to-night is the anniversary of his death, I would fain speak of him for a while."

Ah-Yen paused; I lighted my pipe afresh, and nodded to him to show that I was listening.

"I do not know," he went on, "at what precise time Fifty-Six came into my life. I could indeed find it out by examining my books, but I have never troubled to do so. Naturally I took no more interest in him at first than in any other of my customers—less, perhaps, since he never in the course of our connection brought his clothes to me himself but always sent them by a boy. When I presently perceived that he was becoming one of my regular customers, I allotted to him his number, Fifty-Six, and began to speculate as to who and what he was. Before long I had reached several conclusions in regard to my unknown client. The quality of his linen showed me that, if not rich, he was at any rate fairly well off. I could see that he was a young man of regular Christian life, who went out into society to a certain extent; this I could tell from his sending the same number of articles to the laundry, from his washing always coming on Saturday night, and from the fact that he wore a dress shirt about once

a week.  In disposition he was a modest, unassuming fellow, for his collars were only two inches high."

I stared at Ah-Yen in some amazement, the recent
publications of a favourite novelist had rendered me familiar with this process of analytical reasoning, but I was
prepared for no such revelations from my Eastern friend.

"When I first knew him," Ah-Yen went on, "Fifty-
Six was a student at the university.  This, of course, I
did not know for some time.  I inferred it, however, in
the course of time, from his absence from town during the
four summer months, and from the fact that during the
time of the university examinations the cuffs of his shirts
came to me covered with dates, formulas, and propositions in geometry.  I followed him with no little interest
through his university career.  During the four years
which it lasted, I washed for him every week; my regular
connection with him and the insight which my observation gave me into the lovable character of the man, deep-
ened my first esteem into a profound affection and I became most anxious for his success.  I helped him at each
succeeding examination, as far as lay in my power, by
starching his shirts half-way to the elbow, so as to leave
him as much room as possible for annotations.  My anxiety
during the strain of his final examination I will not attempt to describe.  That Fifty-Six was undergoing the
great crisis of his academic career, I could infer from the
state of his handkerchiefs which, in apparent unconscious-
ness, he used as pen-wipers during the final test.  His conduct throughout the examination bore witness to the moral
development which had taken place in his character during his career as an undergradute; for the notes upon
his cuffs which had been so copious at his earlier examinations were limited now to a few hints, and these upon
topics so intricate as to defy an ordinary memory.  It was

with a thrill of joy that I at last received in his laundry bundle one Saturday early in June, a ruffled dress shirt, the bosom of which was thickly spattered with the spillings of the wine-cup, and realised that Fifty-Six had banqueted as a Bachelor of Arts.

"In the following winter the habit of wiping his pen upon his handkerchief, which I had remarked during his final examination, became chronic with him, and I knew that he had entered upon the study of law. He worked hard during that year, and dress shirts almost disappeared from his weekly bundle. It was in the following winter, the second year of his legal studies, that the tragedy of his life began. I became aware that a change had come over his laundry, from one, or at most two a week, his dress shirts rose to four, and silk handkerchiefs began to replace his linen ones. It dawned upon me that Fifty-Six was abandoning the rigorous tenor of his student life and was going into society. I presently perceived something more; Fifty-Six was in love. It was soon impossible to doubt it. He was wearing seven shirts a week; linen handkerchiefs disappeared from his laundry; his collars rose from two inches to two and a quarter, and finally to two and a half. I have in my possession one of his laundry lists of that period; a glance at it will show the scrupulous care which he bestowed upon his person. Well do I remember the dawning hopes of those days, alternating with the gloomiest despair. Each Saturday I opened his bundle with a trembling eagerness to catch the first signs of a return of his love. I helped my friend in every way that I could. His shirts and collars were masterpieces of my art, though my hand often shook with agitation as I applied the starch. She was a brave noble girl, that I knew; her influence was elevating the whole nature of Fifty-Six; until now he had had in his possession a certain number of detached cuffs and false shirt-fronts. These he discarded now,—at first the false shirt-fronts, scorning the very idea of fraud, and after a time, in his enthusiasm, abandoning even the cuffs. I cannot look back upon those bright happy days of courtship without a sigh.

"The happiness of Fifty-Six seemed to enter into and fill my whole life. I lived but from Saturday to Saturday. The appearance of false shirt-fronts would cast me to the lowest depths of despair; their absence raised me to a pinnacle of hope. It was not till winter softened into spring that Fifty-Six nerved himself to learn his fate. One Saturday he sent me a new white waistcoat, a garment which had hitherto been shunned by his modest nature, to prepare for his use. I bestowed upon it all the resources of my art; I read his purpose in it. On the Saturday following it was returned to me and, with tears of joy, I marked where a warm little hand had rested fondly on the right shoulder, and knew that Fifty-Six was the accepted lover of his sweetheart."

Ah-Yen paused and sat for some time silent; his pipe had sputtered out and lay cold in the hollow of his hand; his eye was fixed upon the wall where the light and shadows shifted in the dull flickering of the candle. At last he spoke again:

"I will not dwell upon the happy days that ensued— days of gaudy summer neckties and white waistcoats, of spotless shirts and lofty collars worn but a single day by the fastidious lover. Our happiness seemed complete and I asked no more from fate. Alas! it was not destined to continue! When the bright days of summer were fading into autumn, I was grieved to notice an occasional quarrel —only four shirts instead of seven, or the reappearance of the abandoned cuffs and shirt-fronts. Reconciliations followed, with tears of penitence upon the shoulder of the white waistcoat, and the seven shirts came back.   But the quarrels grew more frequent and there came at times stormy scenes of passionate emotion that left a track of broken buttons down the waistcoat.   The shirts went slowly down to three, then fell to two, and the collars of my unhappy friend subsided to an inch and three-quarters.   In vain I lavished my utmost care upon Fifty-Six. It seemed to my tortured mind that the gloss upon his shirts and collars would have melted a heart of stone. Alas! my every effort at reconciliation seemed to fail.   An awful month passed; the false fronts and detached cuffs were all back again; the unhappy lover seemed to glory in their perfidy.   At last, one gloomy evening, I found on opening his bundle that he had bought a stock of celluloids, and my heart told me that she had abandoned him for ever.   Of what my poor friend suffered at this time, I can give you no idea; suffice it to say that he passed from celluloid to a blue flannel shirt and from blue to grey.   The sight of a red cotton handkerchief in his wash at length warned me that his disappointed love had unhinged his mind, and I feared the worst.   Then came an agonising interval of three weeks during which he sent me nothing, and after that came the last parcel that I ever received from him—an enormous bundle that seemed to contain all his effects.   In this, to my horror, I discovered one shirt the breast of which was stained a deep crimson with his blood, and pierced by a ragged hole that showed where a bullet had singed through into his heart.

"A fortnight before, I remembered having heard the street boys crying the news of an appalling suicide, and I know now that it must have been he.   After the first shock of my grief had passed, I sought to keep him in my memory by drawing the portrait which hangs beside you. I have some skill in the art, and I feel assured that I have caught the expression of his face. The picture is, of course, an ideal one, for, as you know, I never saw Fifty-Six."

The bell on the door of the outer shop tinkled at the entrance of a customer. Ah-Yen rose with that air of quiet resignation that habitually marked his demeanour, and remained for some time in the shop. When he returned he seemed in no mood to continue speaking of his lost friend. I left him soon after and walked sorrowfully home to my lodgings. On my way I mused much upon my little Eastern friend and the sympathetic grasp of his imagination. But a burden lay heavy on my heart—something I would fain have told him but which I could not bear to mention. I could not find it in my heart to shatter the airy castle of his fancy. For my life has been secluded and lonely and I have known no love like that of my ideal friend. Yet I have a haunting recollection of a certain huge bundle of washing that I sent to him about a year ago. I had been absent from town for three weeks and my laundry was much larger than usual in consequence. And if I mistake not there was in the bundle a tattered shirt that had been grievously stained by the breaking of a bottle of red ink in my portmanteau, and burnt in one place where an ash fell from my cigar as I made up the bundle. Of all this I cannot feel absolutely certain, yet I know at least that until a year ago, when I transferred my custom to a more modern establishment, my laundry number with Ah-Yen was Fifty-Six.

# My Victorian Girlhood

### By *Lady Nearleigh Slopover*

THE life we led at Gloops—Gloops was my father's seat—
had all the charm and quiet and order which went with
life in my young days. My dear Papa (he was the eleventh Baron Gloops) was most strict in his household. As
a nobleman of the old school, he believed fully in the
maxim *noblesse oblige*. He always insisted on the servants
assembling for prayers at eight every morning. Indeed
his first question to his own man when he brought up his
brandy and soda at ten was whether the servants had been
at prayers at eight.

My dear Mama too always seemed to fulfil my idea of
what a *grande dame* should be. She fully understood the
routine of a great house like Gloops, and had a wonderful
knowledge, not only of the kitchen, but of all sorts of
draughts, simples and samples and the use of herbs. If
any of the maids was ill, Mama never called a doctor but
herself mixed up a draught from roots that would have
the girl on her feet in half an hour.

Nor did she disdain to do things herself, especially in
an emergency. Once when Papa was taken faint in the
drawing room, Mama herself rang the bell for an egg,
told the butler to hand her a glass and a decanter and
herself broke the egg into the glass with her own hands.
Papa revived at the sight of her presence of mind and himself reached for the brandy.

To myself and my younger sister, Lucy, Papa and Mama
were ideal parents. Never a day passed but Papa would

either come up to our nursery himself, and chat with our governess, Mademoiselle Fromage—one of the De Bries— or would at least send up his own man to ask how we were. Even as quite little girls Papa could tell us apart without difficulty.

Mama too was devoted to us, and would let us come down to her boudoir and see her all dressed to go out to a dinner, or let us come and speak to her when she was ready to drive in the phaeton; and once when Lucy was ill Mama sent her own maid to sleep in Lucy's room, in spite of the infection.

Gloops was on the border of Lincolnshire. All of Papa's tenants and cottagers spoke with the beautiful old broad accent of the fen country and said "Yowp" for "yes," and "Nowp" for "no," and "Thowp" for "thou," and "cowp" for "soup." It seems so musical. It is a pity it is dying out.

Papa was a model landlord. The tenantry were never evicted unless they failed to pay their rent, and when the cottages fell down Papa had them propped up again. Once a year Papa gave a great ball for the tenantry on his estate, and our friends used to drive long distances to be there, and the great hall was cleared for dancing, for the gentry, and the tenantry danced in the great barn. Papa gave each of them a bun and an orange and a prayer book for each child. The working class was happier, I think, in those days.

Papa was not only democratic in that way with his tenantry but also with the people of the neighbourhood and of the village, though none of them were gentlemen. Quite often he would bring Dr. McGregor, the doctor of the village, to dine at Gloops, I mean if no one else was there. Dr. McGregor had taken a very high degree at Edinburgh, but was not a gentleman. He had travelled a great deal and had been decorated by the King of France for some wonderful medical work for the French armies in Algeria, so it was a pity that he wasn't a gentleman: especially as you couldn't tell that he wasn't if no one said so.

Isolated as Gloops was, many great people drove down from London to see us, on account of Papa's position in the Lords. Indeed the most wonderful thing about our life as children at Gloops was the visit every now and then of one of these great and distinguished people whose names are now history. How well one remembers them—such old world manners and courtesy! I recall how Lucy and I were brought into the drawing room to shake hands with dear old Lord Melrush, the prime minister—always so pleasant and jolly. I remember Mama said, "These are my two little girls"—and Lord Melrush laughed and said, "Well, thank God they don't look like their father, eh?" Which was really quite clever of him, because we didn't. And I remember old Field Marshal Lord Stickett, perhaps England's greatest strategist—they called him Wellington's right hand man—he'd lost his left arm. I can still see him standing on the hearth rug saying, "Your two little girls, ma'am: well, I don't think much of them!" He was always like that, concise and abrupt.

I liked much better Admiral Rainbow, who had been one of Nelson's captains and had a black patch over his eye where someone hit him in the face at Trafalgar. I was quite a growing girl when he came, fourteen at least, and he said, "By Gad! Madam, shiver my spankers, but here's a gal for you! Look at the stern run under her counter!"

Another great thing in the life at Gloops was when I got old enough to dine with Mama and Papa and their guests. Such dinners were a wonderful education. I was

taken into dinner once by Lord Glower the great archaeol-
ogist. He hardly spoke. I asked him if he thought the
Pyramids were built by the Hittites. He said he didn't
know.

We used to dine in the old wainscotted dining hall—
it was a marvellous room, dating from Richard III with
the panels all worm-eaten almost to pieces. Papa was offered huge sums for them. It had some grand old paint-
ings—one a Vandyke, so blackened you couldn't possibly
tell what it was especially as most of the paint had fallen
off: Papa later on presented it to the Nation—the year the
prime minister voted him the Garter—refusing any pay
for it, though the Prime Minister made him accept a thousand guineas as a *solatium*. Papa fetched down another
Vandyke from the storeroom.

By the time I was eighteen I think I may claim to have
grown to be a very handsome girl and certainly, as everybody said, very aristocratic looking. I was several times
compared with the Princess Eulalie of Anheuser and once
with the Grand Duchess Marianna Maria of Swig-Pilsener.
Dear old Dr. Glowworm, our Vicar, who was so old that
he remembered the French Revolution, said that if I had
lived then I would certainly have been guillotined, or at
least shut up.

But presently there came into my life—a little earlier
than that, I was eighteen—the greatest event of all, when
I first met Alfred my dear husband that was to be. It
was at a great dinner party that Papa gave at Gloops, given
for Sir John Overdraft, the head of the new bank that had
just made Papa a director. Sir John was the head of the
bank and had been knighted, but the strange thing was
that he was really nobody. I mean he had made a great
fortune in the City and had huge influence in finance, but
he wasn't anybody. And, what was more, everybody knew

that he was nobody. Papa made no secret of it. I remember hearing old Lord Tweedlepip, our neighbour, in the drawing room before dinner ask Papa who Sir John was and Papa said, "As far as I know he isn't anybody." But in meeting with him Papa was all courtesy itself; indeed he often explained to us children that even though prominent people—writers, painters, sculptors, for instance—were often nobody, we should treat them in society as if they were like ourselves.

It was such a large party that I can hardly remember all the people, especially as it was my first real dinner party. I was out, but hadn't yet been presented. But there was one man there I especially noticed, although he was not only nobody but was an American. He was the first I think I ever saw, though now of course you meet them anywhere, and many of them such cultivated people that you can hardly tell them. But this man, the first American I saw, seemed different from the men around him, more hard and dangerous, and yet pleasant enough, but no manners. I couldn't even be sure of his name because Papa and Sir John, who both seemed to know him well, kept calling him different things like "Old Forty-four Calibre," and "Old Ten-Spot." His family seat was called Colorado and I gathered that he owned gold mines. I gathered all this because I happened to be near the library door a little before dinner, when Papa and Sir John and Mr. Derringer—that perhaps was his real name —were all talking together. Mr. Derringer wanted to give Papa an enormous part of a gold mine and then Papa was to pass it on to Sir John and the new bank was to pass it over to the public. It all seemed very generous. I heard Mr. Derringer say to Papa, laughing, "Gloops, if we had you in the States you would be sent to Sing-Sing in six months." Sing-Sing it seems was a new place they had just started in America. It corresponds, Mama said, to our House of Commons. Mr. Derringer laughed when he said that Papa could get in, but I am sure he meant it.

But I am leaving out, in a feminine way, I fear, the great thing of the evening which was that it was dear Alfred, my later husband, who took me in to dinner. So wonderful he looked, over six feet high and as straight as a piece of wood, with beautiful brown hair and those handsome high side whiskers—the French call them *cotelette de mouton*—which were worn then. I had never seen him before and all that I knew of him was that his name was the Hon. Alfred Cyril Nancie Slopover, eldest son of the tenth Marquis of Slopover and Bath and that his people were west county people, but very old and very good. His mother was a Dudd, which made her a first cousin of Lord Havengotteny.

Alfred, I say, took me in. We hardly spoke at dinner because I think I was shy, and at any rate, at our end of the table Mr. Derringer was telling Mama wonderful stories about hunting the wild papooses in Colorado, which must be fascinating, and how the Cactus Indians pursue the buffalo with affidavits, and we were all listening. But Alfred, though he never talked much, had that firm incisive way of saying things, just in a word, that sounds so final. For instance, after dinner, when the men came into the drawing room for tea, I said to Alfred, "Shall we go into the conservatory?" And he said, "Let's." And I said, "Shall we sit among the begonias?" and he said, "Rather!" and after a time I said, "Shall we go back to the drawing room?", and he said, "Ah!" When we got back to the drawing room, Mr. Derringer was still telling Mama of his wonderful adventures—indeed they were all listening.

It made me realize what a vast country America is. In fact I have always felt, and still feel, that some day it will have a great future. But that evening I could hardly listen to Mr. Derringer because my heart was beating so with happiness, as I felt certain that Alfred had fallen in love with me. He looked so noble, sitting there listening to Mr. Derringer, with his mouth half open, seeming to drink it all in. Now and again he would make such intelligent comments as when Mr. Derringer told about the social life in the West, and the lynching parties, and of how they invite even the negroes to them, and Alfred said, "Do they really!" He seemed that evening, in fact he always has seemed, so typically British, so willing to be informed.

Everybody was so loud in praise of Alfred next day. Tiptoeing round the house, because I did not think it dishonourable, I was able to hear such a lot of complimentary things about him. Mr. Derringer, who used a lot of those fascinating American expressions taken from their machinery, called him a "complete nut," and Lord John, who is so brusque and quick himself that he admires Alfred's dreamy, poetical nature, said he seemed "only half there." But think of my delight when a day or two later Alfred sent Mama a beautiful bouquet of roses from Slops, his father's seat, and then a basket of hothouse grapes and then, for Papa, a large fish, a salmon. Two weeks after that, he wrote and definitely proposed to Papa, and Papa went up to London and saw the solicitors and accepted Alfred. It all seemed so romantic and wonderful, and then Alfred came over for a blissful week at Gloops as my betrothed, which meant that we could walk in the grounds together by ourselves, and that even in the drawing room Mama would sit at the other end of the room and pretend not to see us.

Of course Love always has its ups and downs and never

runs smooth: I remember that there was a dreadful quarrel with my sister Lucy who said that Alfred was ignorant and didn't *know* anything: and I said why should he? What did a man like Alfred need to know? It seemed so silly. I remember I often thought of it later on when Lucy made her own unhappy marriage.

Then for a little while there was a little trouble about my dowry, or jointure. Papa at first offered five thousand pounds and Alfred refused it flat. He said he ought to have at least ten thousand. It seemed so romantic to be quarrelled over like that, as a sort of gauge of battle. Alfred was so firm: even when Papa raised from pounds to guineas he held out. So at last Papa gave way completely, and not only gave way, but went generously further and gave Alfred twelve thousand pounds, all to be paid in shares in Mr. Derringer's gold mine. Papa explained that they were called "preferred" shares, which made them very desirable. He said that if Alfred and I kept them long enough there was no telling what they would be worth. So Alfred was delighted at his victory over Papa, especially as Sir John always said that Papa could have been a financier and Mr. Derringer had said he could have got into Sing-Sing.

I remember that Papa, in the same generous fit gave away a lot of the same gold shares, practically all he had, to various people, to Alfred's father, Lord Slopover, to old Lord Tweedlepip, our neighbour and others, for next to nothing, or at least nothing like their real value.

Then came the happy day when Alfred and I were married in the little church at Gloops, by old Dr. Glowworm. Everybody was there, and all the tenantry and cottagers in a long line outside the church, for Alfred and me to walk through; and Papa gave a grand fête for the tenantry on the lawn with beer to drink our health in and an orange and bun for each of the children, and a work-box for each grown-up girl, a work-basket each for the old women, and for each young boy a book called *Work*. I think the working people were far happier then than now. They often strike me now as restless. I think they need more work.

After our marriage we went to live in London because the Prime Minister wanted Alfred to go into the House, as he said that England needed men like Alfred. Alfred accepted the seat but on the firm condition that he needn't speak, or work, or attend or have anything to do with the voters. The Prime Minister said yes at once: he didn't want Alfred to see the voters at all.

Naturally, of course, our earlier married life had its ups and downs as it does with all people. When we first went to London we were quite poor, I mean not at all well off, and it was difficult for us to afford enough servants to manage our house properly: on the other hand, without a house that size it would have been hard to use all our servants. Even as it was Alfred would himself often fetch up his own shaving water, and more than once I have seen him light his own fire, touch the match to it himself, sooner than ring up a servant. But we both agreed that these little discomforts only make life all the more worthy.

But after a little while Papa's influence got for Alfred a court appointment as Gentleman Equerry of the Bloodhounds, which made our position much easier. Alfred, of course, didn't have to take the bloodhounds out himself, as that was done by the Yeoman Equerry: but he had to countersign all the warrants for what they ate, which often kept him busy.

Then on top of little hardships at home came the terrible trouble of my poor sister Lucy's marriage. Lucy had always, I think, been a little wanting in making proper social distinctions.  I remember that even as a girl she would often speak with cottagers in what seemed quite a wrong way, as if she were their equal.  So in a way it was not surprising when she married absolutely beneath her. Papa and Mama were utterly consternated when they heard of it and Mama decided to do the only brave thing about it and not speak to Lucy any more.  She had married a man who not only had no family—I mean in the literal sense absolutely none—but who worked as a journalist on a newspaper.  I know that of course nowadays things are different and a journalist can be received anywhere, I mean if he is properly born.  But it was not so then and Lucy's husband, whose name was Mr. Smith, was even worse than that as he had tried to write books as well: indeed he had one published, a book about flowers and botany.  The whole thing was of course a great pity to us—I mean, Lucy's living like that—until at last Papa, who naturally had great influence, got the Colonial Office to pay Mr. Smith's expenses, with Lucy and the children—there were three already—to go out to British Borneo to study flowers: as he couldn't afford to get back, they all stayed there and it was all right.  Papa had a letter later from one of the boys from Sarawak and Papa said he seemed promising and might grow up to be a Dacoit.

But much more serious were the financial troubles which once or twice threatened to overwhelm us.  The first was when Papa's bank broke and Sir John and the directors went to jail, because in those days the law was very strict and fair and the bank directors went to jail like anybody else—except of course Papa.  In his case, as the Lord Chief Justice explained, it had to be understood that he acted in utter ignorance, in fact that he knew nothing, being a nobleman.  Indeed Lord Argue, after sentencing the directors, complimented Papa very highly: he said it was men like Papa who make embezzlement possible—which we all thought very handsome. But after all it was a great relief when it was over, especially as it turned out that by a lucky chance Papa had sold all his own shares in the bank the very day before it broke.

But to us, to Alfred and me, a much more direct blow was the failure of Mr. Derringer's gold mine. We never knew just what had happened. It seemed that the mine had not exactly failed but it had never been there. Alfred heard in the City that Mr. Derringer had "salted" the mine but Alfred couldn't see how he could do that, as it would take such a lot. At any rate it was all in the American papers and poor Mr. Derringer's trial and he was sent to prison for ten years and was there for weeks and weeks before he could get out. Papa's name came into it all, of course, as a first director but he was out of it since, though there might have been a sort of scandal except that the American judge spoke very handsomely of Papa's ignorance of it all. Indeed he said that what Papa didn't know would fill a book, and that it was men like Papa who gave England the name it had.

So it all blew over, but presently Alfred and I found that after that the dividends from the mine stopped, which we couldn't understand as they were preferred. Alfred would have been very cool with Papa over it, but as Papa was getting old it seemed wrong to get cool with him. If anything happened to Papa while Alfred was cool, it might make a difference. Indeed it was just at that time that dear Papa got a stroke, his first stroke. It didn't really incapacitate him at first but we thought best to call in a consultant opinion, and then he got a second stroke, and so, in real alarm, we sent for a great Harley Street specialist and Papa got a third stroke.  With the third stroke, he passed out.

I will not carry these Memoirs down any further than the day of Papa's funeral, which seems a good place to stop.  Such a wonderful day, one of those bright, crisp autumn days when it just feels good to be alive!  Gloops looked so wonderful in the bright sunlight and everywhere the late autumn flowers.  And such wonderful messages of sympathy!  One from the House of Lords, official, to say that the House had learned with satisfaction that Lord Gloops was to be buried; and one from the Home Secretary expressing his personal appreciation of Papa's burial: and one from the Secretary in Waiting at Windsor Castle that the whole court was ordered to go into half mourning for a quarter of an hour.  And then the funeral service in our dear little church at Gloops.  Old Dr. Glowworm, though he must have been nearly a hundred at the time, preached the funeral sermon.  It was just a little hard to hear him, except the text which was "Where has he gone?"—we all thought it so beautifully apt—but we couldn't quite follow Dr. Glowworm's answer.  Then as the crowning thing in the day came the reading of Papa's will, by Papa's own solicitor, Mr. Rust, who came from London to Gloops on purpose.  Of course we knew that everything would be all right but, of course, couldn't help feeling a little nervous.  Poor Papa had always been a little uncertain and when we remembered about Papa's bank and the mine, we couldn't feel quite sure what would happen to Gloops.  The title, of course, would go to my cousin, the present Marquis of Gloops, but the entail had been cut long ago and Papa was free to do as he liked.  I remember how dear Alfred sat so bolt upright, trying so hard to understand every word, though of course that was impossible as most of the will was in law terms. But the meaning came out clear enough. Dear Papa had done everything just as it should be according to the fine old traditions of the time. Mama was given the Dower House for life, with the full right to use her own money in maintaining it. All the old servants were remembered—Papa gave them each a suit of mourning and quite a substantial sum; I forget what, but I think at least ten pounds, which meant a great deal to people in their class. For my sister Lucy, Papa could not, of course, in view of what had happened, do very much: but even in her case he left her something to remember him by, a beautiful set of books from his library—sermons bound in old leather—and a purse for each of her children—there were only five at that time—with half a sovereign in it, and a prayer book each. Alfred and I got Gloops and all the residuum—that was the word Mr. Rust used—residuum of the estate, which was only fair as we should need it to keep the estate up: on the other hand we could hardly have used the residuum if we hadn't had the estate itself. Mr. Rust explained it all very clearly.

After it was all over Alfred said, "Well, it's all over."

# The Hidden Secret of the City

*That It Still Dreams of the Farm*

EVERY year when the good old summertime begins I feel that longing to turn my back—all of it—on the city, which is probably felt by nine city dwellers out of ten. Not for me the roar of the metropolis. Let me feel the new-mown hay blow in my face and let me hear the trout stream gurgle under the fallen logs in the bush. I know all that can be said in favor of the city. I admit that it palpitates with intellectual life, that it throbs with the conscious power of collective thought. But not for me— not a palpitation, not a throb!

The truth is, and I don't mind admitting it at this time of year, I am afraid, and always have been, of a great city and of the kind of people who live in it. Like everybody else who has come off a farm—our homestead was in Georgina Township, up in Ontario; perhaps you know it?—I have never felt at ease with high class city people, with financial magnates, great criminal lawyers, bank presidents and scintillating literary wits. I always felt that the wits might start something or the magnates sit on something or the great criminal lawyer might say something. Anybody from the country knows the feeling. As to the bankers, everybody knows that these men hold the world in the hollow of their hand; if they lift their thumb over we go. So I am uneasy with them. I don't want them to lift it while I'm round.

But that feeling is all gone since an experience I had just a little while ago. It was my fate to have to give an address at one of the biggest luncheon clubs on the *Diplomatic Situation in Europe,* in one of the biggest hotels of one of our cities before some of the biggest men in the country. If anything sounds bigger than that, I don't hear it. It was certainly a distinguished crowd. As I looked round at the vast glittering hotel dining-room, filled with hundreds and hundreds of what I knew were typical city men, leaders in business and finance and the professions, I felt appalled. It seemed impossible that I could dare to speak to them.

So there I sat, at the head of the table, in the very centre of that marvellous gathering, making conversation as best I could. Beside me was the president of one of the biggest banks in the world, a fine, dignified man who looked the part. I wouldn't have dared to borrow $5 from him, if I was dying.

I talked as best I could; and presently, by chance, I mentioned Ohio. "I come from there," he said, and then added, as if owning up to something, like an honest man, "we had a farm there; as a matter of fact, I have it still." The moment he said that I felt easier. "Did you?" I said. "I was brought up on a farm in Ontario—Georgina Township—we had a hundred acres, counting the bush." "We had more than that," said the bank president; "we had over five hundred"—then he realized, like the kindly man he is, that he had said a rather brutal thing, as between farmers, and he added at once: "Of course, the old homestead wasn't as much as that at first; we only had a quarter section less sixty acres. But later when Uncle Bill went out West we had his half section, less the road allowance of four rods that went right across the place just behind the homestead."

The words were like music! "Quarter sections" and "homesteads," and relations called "Uncle Bill," and things measured in "rods"! That's the language I like to hear! I felt at home at once.

With that we were started. Five minutes later, if the conversation of that great financier had been reported, it would have run like this: "You can do better with soy beans for hogs than you can in trying to raise grain for them. Put in your soy beans, with a cover crop first—"

But I had to interrupt him there. "Soy beans are all right," I said, "if the land is clean enough." And with that we were absorbed; gone was all the glitter and the form and pomp of the occasion. The bank president was back in Ohio and I was back in Georgina Township (next to North Gwillimbury, you can't miss it; take the town line past the old Prosser place) and he was feeding hogs on soy beans, and I was objecting that if he didn't raise any wheat he'd have no straw for bedding, and he admitted it. Think of a man in his position sleeping on straw!

All of a sudden I remembered, we both seemed to remember, where we were. Imagine talking farm stuff in a gathering like that! And in the silence that fell for the moment between us, I listened and caught a little of the talk of the group of men—presidents of this, and vice-presidents of that—who sat at the table just beneath the head table that was ours. One man I noticed in particular, a dignified figure, the face of a diplomat. He was saying to the man beside him: "Don't talk to me of leghorn hens! I won't have them on my place. You waste your money in trying to put a twelve-foot wire fence round a leghorn, and even then they'll fly over it. No, sir, I admit they lay, but give me a heavy fowl, a Barred Rock or a Black Jersey Giant, and you've got something! They'll lay pretty good, and they're a table bird and you don't have to chase them all over the place!"

"But wait a minute," objected the man next to him. "You can't make them pay!"

I listened, fascinated! They were talking of that wonderful, vital question, "Can hens be made to pay?"

"They do pay!" said the first man. "Out at my place in Indiana last week we showed a clear profit on them!"

He didn't say how much: no one was cruel enough to ask. But I knew, because my hens back in Ontario have been showing a clear profit right along, a total of sixty cents in November (and mind, I've only two hundred hens) and eight cents in December and this last month over a dollar! So I understood just what was meant. That banker, I suppose, wouldn't take any special joy in a corporation that would pay a dividend on $5,000,000; but to make a profit, an actual profit, on hens (not counting, of course, your own time, nor the hired man's time, nor the odd months when they don't lay)—Ah! that is high finance!

So after that I felt easier. And when I realized that my neighbour on the left was talking about trout fishing in an Indiana creek, and the man next him was spearing suckers with a jack light, then it was all too easy.

So when I got up to speak I knew that I was among friends, men whose thoughts I could share, whose sympathies I could call forth.

"In rising, gentlemen," I said, "to speak on this matter of the Diplomatic Situation in Europe, I find myself in no little difficulty. I have just come down here from my farm—a little place that I call my farm—in Simcoe County, Ontario, where I have, gentlemen, nearly ten acres, without counting two acres of bush."

I could feel a distinct wave of interest pass over the audience. They seemed to draw their chairs sympathetically nearer to me.

"Yes, gentlemen," I continued, "ten acres and a little bush. The bush, I admit, is mostly soft maple and ash with a little black birch, and I know that you will at once tell me that you don't call that first-class hard wood. No, neither do I. But it is easy to cut, gentlemen, and you can get in there with your portable saw most any time. But, as I say, in regard to this Diplomatic Situation in Europe, I went up to my place then—it's just off the Muskoka Highway; if any of you come up ask at Hatley's store—to work up this question, and I found it hard to do so. You see, gentlemen, we had, in our section, as no doubt you had, a rather mean spring this year—an early thaw that took off the snow and that sharp frost that winter-killed a lot of the fall wheat."

All over the audience I could see men nodding in confirmation. "It hit the apple trees hard, gentlemen; I lost about half a dozen McIntosh red, just coming nicely into bearing. I know you'll at once all ask me why I hadn't banked them up with manure in the fall. Well, I'll tell you, gentlemen, I don't believe in it. No, sir!"

I could sense sensation, denial and corroboration rippling all round among the audience.

"I hold that if you bank up your young trees that way, you *soften* them. They lose body and the fruit is never really firm; and, what's more, gentlemen, you have all kinds of bugs, as you know, getting round your roots. Well, I wouldn't enlarge on it!"

I could hear a sigh of disappointment.

"All I'm saying," I went on, "is that what with one thing and another there was too much to do round the place to let me get at this question of the Diplomatic Situation in Europe, on which I was invited here to address you. You know how crowded a man gets on a little place like that, especially just at seeding time with everything coming on at once. You haven't the leisure, the spare time, of city folks. And then I was specially anxious, gentlemen, as soon as the spell of really fine weather should set in, I was specially anxious to have another try at early cucumbers. I don't know whether any of you gentlemen have ever tried early cucumbers—"

Had they? I could see by the thrill of excitement, the tenseness of this luncheon audience, that they all had!

"But if you *have*, then you know that early cucumbers are a mighty speculative thing! It takes nerve! One nasty frost and you may lose a dozen plants at a crack. You don't feel safe, at least not up with us, not clear through till the first of June. You can start them all right, that's not the trouble, I admit, but it's when you come to *set them out!*"

They were listening, breathless.

"The gentleman sitting next to me but one—who is, I understand, a member of your State Senate—says he does fairly well with his cucumbers by starting them in a greenhouse. He says that last year he had eight, or was it nine, really fine plants, started that way, though he admits he took a lot of trouble with them. But I don't think, gentlemen, that you'll ever enjoy the flavour in a cucumber started in a greenhouse. Now, I'll tell you my plan—and I give it you for what it's worth."

There was tense excitement now all over the audience.

"You take an old sod and cut it with your jack-knife into about a four-inch square, turn it upside down and put your seed into that!"

Sensation!

"Then take your sods and set them in rows in a hot bed with lots of first-class manure, gentlemen—and I know I need not tell men like you that when I say manure, I mean real manure with lots of body, not just a lot of dry straw. You want heat. But I need not tell men like you what manure is. Use lots of it and tramp it well down, till you're satisfied. Give it a four-inch layer of the best dirt you can lay your hands on, put your sods on, and you'll get real results.

"But what I mean about this Diplomatic Situation in Europe is that I didn't get time to work it up; in fact, to be quite frank, I'll go so far as to say that I don't give a damn about it anyway! I'd rather be up on my ten-acre farm setting out cucumbers than loafing round all the Chancelleries of Europe, or whatever they call them— and unless I am much mistaken, so would you, every one of you!"

There was deafening applause. They said it was one of the finest talks they'd heard for years. And later the reporters of the papers—you know how clever those boys are—had it all fixed up under the heading *"Home Agricultural Interest First Claim on Nation,"* and so I saw what I had really meant.

But meantime I had drifted out of the place and over to one of the big city clubs, feeling pretty well elated. Till now, though my friends have often been kind enough to put me up, I've been afraid to go into those metropolitan Clubs. But this time I walked into the lounge-room of one of the swellest of them with absolute confidence. I was beginning to understand the city.

It was the quiet hour of the club day, the early afternoon. There was hardly anyone in the lounge except a couple of ministers—clergymen. I knew what they were by their quiet black dress and their kind serious faces. One of them, I could see by his gaiters, must be an Episcopal bishop. I didn't want to overhear their talk, as I felt sure it would deal with some of their spiritual minis-

trations, and be, in a way, private.  But I couldn't help it.
The Bishop was saying:

"Then just as she seemed to be getting along so well,
something went wrong."  He paused and shook his head
and repeated "something went wrong!"

"Till then," the other asked anxiously, "she had seemed
quite all right?"

"Quite," said the Bishop.  "Quite!  A little restless, perhaps, at times.  But then I thought that meant merely
that the flies were troubling her.  She'd been giving eight
to ten quarts every morning and at least six at night. . . ."

"Perhaps," said the other in gentle admonishment, "perhaps you put her on the grass too early?"

"She hadn't been on the grass," said the Bishop slowly,
and added with a groan, "We were still feeding her chop!"

There was a pause, I could see that they were old friends,
and that argument was painful to them, yet the lesser
clergyman said firmly, "I know we mustn't dispute it
again; but don't you think, perhaps, that Holsteins—I say
it with all gentleness . . ."

I rose and moved quietly away.  I knew that they were
going to talk of the unsolved problem of the Holstein
versus the Jersey cow, beside which squaring the circle is
child's play: but I couldn't bear to hear it; our last little
Jersey—but no, no, never mind.  The country, too, like
the city, has its sharp tragedies.

           .    .    .    .    .    .    .

So now, I know the city and I'm not afraid of it.  I
understand city men.  As they sit in their palatial hotels
they are dreaming of morning mists rising off the pasture
in the river valley.  As they study at their meals their bills
of fare, they are not looking at such items as Pâté Bour-
guignon à la Marengo, which the Chef sticks on the list
to remind himself of France.  What they are trying to find

is Flop-Over pancakes, Honey, and Liver and Bacon à la Wabash.   And when the orchestra starts its softest music, they'll close their eyes and hear the drone of the cow-bells in the bush.

The Great City!   There's no such place.   It's just where people go, bravely enough, to earn the money to get back home.

I know now that I can go down to Wall Street, New York, with a bag of soy beans under one arm and a hen under the other, and borrow all the money I want.

# The Mariposa Bank Mystery

SUICIDE is a thing that ought not to be committed without very careful thought. It often involves serious consequences, and in some cases brings pain to others than oneself.

I don't say that there is no justification for it. There often is. Anybody who has listened to certain kinds of music, or read certain kinds of poetry, or heard certain kinds of performances upon the concertina, will admit that there are some lives which ought not to be continued, and that even suicide has its brighter aspects.

But to commit suicide on grounds of love is at the best a very dubious experiment. I know that in this I am expressing an opinion contrary to that of most true lovers who embrace suicide on the slightest provocation as the only honourable termination of an existence that never ought to have begun.

I quite admit that there is a glamour and a sensation about the thing which has its charm, and that there is nothing like it for causing a girl to realize the value of the heart that she has broken and which breathed forgiveness upon her at the very moment when it held in its hand the half-pint of prussic acid that was to terminate its beating for ever.

But apart from the general merits of the question, I suppose there are few people, outside of lovers, who know what it is to commit suicide four times in five weeks.

Yet this was what happened to Mr. Pupkin, of the Exchange Bank of Mariposa.

Ever since he had known Zena Pepperleigh he had

realized that his love for her was hopeless. She was too beautiful for him and too good for him; her father hated him and her mother despised him; his salary was too small and his own people were too rich.

If you add to all that that he came up to the judge's house one night and found a poet reciting verses to Zena, you will understand the suicide at once. It was one of those regular poets with a solemn jackass face, and lank parted hair and eyes like puddles of molasses. I don't know how he came there—up from the city, probably—but there he was on the Pepperleighs' verandah that August evening. He was reciting poetry—either Tennyson's or Shelley's, or his own, you couldn't tell—and about him sat Zena with her hands clasped and Nora Gallagher looking at the sky and Jocelyn Drone gazing into infinity, and a little tubby woman looking at the poet with her head falling over sideways—in fact, there was a whole group of them.

.    .    .    .    .    .    .

I don't know what it is about poets that draws women to them in this way. But everybody knows that a poet has only to sit and saw the air with his hands and recite verses in a deep stupid voice, and all the women are crazy over him. Men despise him and would kick him off the verandah if they dared, but the women simply rave over him.

So Pupkin sat there in the gloom and listened to this poet reciting Browning and he realized that everybody understood it but him. He could see Zena with her eyes fixed on the poet as if she were hanging on to every syllable (she was; she needed to), and he stood it just about fifteen minutes and then slid off the side of the verandah and disappeared without even saying good-night.

He walked straight down Oneida Street and along the Main Street just as hard as he could go. There was only one purpose in his mind,—suicide. He was heading straight for Jim Eliot's drug store on the main corner and his idea was to buy a drink of chloroform and drink it and die right there on the spot.

As Pupkin walked down the street, the whole thing was so vivid in his mind that he could picture it to the remotest detail. He could even see it all in type, in big headings in the newspapers of the following day:

APPALLING SUICIDE
PETER PUPKIN POISONED

He perhaps hoped that the thing might lead to some kind of public enquiry and that the question of Browning's poetry and whether it is altogether fair to allow of its general circulation would be fully ventilated in the newspapers.

Thinking all that, Pupkin came to the main corner.

On a warm August evening the drug store of Mariposa, as you know, is all a blaze of lights. You can hear the hissing of the soda-water fountain half a block away, and inside the store there are ever so many people—boys and girls and old people too—all drinking sarsaparilla and chocolate sundaes and lemon sours and foaming drinks that you take out of long straws. There is such a laughing and a talking as you never heard, and the girls are all in white and pink and cambridge blue, and the soda fountain is of white marble with silver taps, and it hisses and sputters, and Jim Eliot and his assistant wear white coats with red geraniums in them, and it's all just as gay as gay.

The foyer of the opera in Paris may be a fine sight, but

I doubt if it can compare with the inside of Eliot's drug store in Mariposa—for real gaiety and joy of living.

This night the store was especially crowded because it was a Saturday and that meant early closing for all the hotels, except, of course, Smith's.   So as the hotels were shut, the people were all in the drug store, drinking like fishes.   It just shows the folly of Local Option and the Temperance Movement and all that.   Why, if you shut the hotels you simply drive the people to the soda fountains and there's more drinking than ever, and not only of the men, too, but the girls and young boys and children.   I've seen little things of eight and nine that had to be lifted up on the high stools at Eliot's drug store, drinking great goblets of lemon soda, enough to burst them—brought there by their own fathers, and why?  Simply because the hotel bars were shut.

What's the use of thinking you can stop people drinking merely by cutting off whiskey and brandy?   The only effect is to drive them to taking lemon sour and sarsaparilla and cherry pectoral and caroka cordial and things they wouldn't have touched before.   So in the long run they drink more than ever.   The point is that you can't prevent people having a good time, no matter how hard you try.   If they can't have it with lager beer and brandy, they'll have it with plain soda and lemon pop, and so the whole gloomy scheme of the temperance people breaks down, anyway.

But I was only saying that Eliot's drug store in Mariposa on a Saturday night is the gayest and brightest spot in the world.

And just imagine what a fool of a place to commit suicide in!

Just imagine going up to the soda-water fountain and

asking for five cents' worth of chloroform and soda! Well, you simply can't, that's all.

That's the way Pupkin found it. You see, as soon as he came in, somebody called out: "Hello, Pete!" and one or two others called "Hullo, Pup!" and some said: "How goes it?" and others: "How are you toughing it?" and so on, because you see they had all been drinking more or less and naturally they felt jolly and gladhearted.

So the upshot of it was that instead of taking chloroform, Pupkin stepped up to the counter of the fountain and he had a bromo-seltzer with cherry soda, and after that he had one of those aerated seltzers, and then a couple of lemon seltzers and a bromophizzer.

I don't know if you know the mental effect of a bromoseltzer.

But it's a hard thing to commit suicide on.

You can't.

You feel so buoyant.

Anyway, what with the phizzing of the seltzer and the lights and the girls, Pupkin began to feel so fine that he didn't care a cuss for all the Browning in the world, and as for the poet—oh, to blazes with him! What's poetry, anyway?—only rhymes.

So, would you believe it, in about ten minutes Peter Pupkin was off again and heading straight for the Pepperleighs' house, poet or no poet, and, what was more to the point, he carried with him three great bricks of Eliot's ice cream—in green, pink, and brown layers. He struck the verandah just at the moment when Browning was getting too stale and dreary for words. His brain was all sizzling and jolly with the bromo-seltzer, and when he fetched out the ice cream bricks and Zena ran to get plates and spoons to eat it with, and Pupkin went with her to help fetch them and they picked out the spoons together, they were so laughing and happy that it was just a marvel. Girls, you know, need no bromo-seltzer. They're full of it all the time.

And as for the poet—well, can you imagine how Pupkin felt when Zena told him that the poet was married, and that the tubby little woman with her head on sideways was his wife?

So they had the ice cream, and the poet ate it in bucketsful. Poets always do. They need it. And after it the poet recited some stanzas of his own and Pupkin saw that he had misjudged the man, because it was dandy poetry, the very best. That night Pupkin walked home on air and there was no thought of chloroform, and it turned out that he hadn't committed suicide, but like all lovers he had commuted it.

.    .    .    .    .    .    .

I don't need to describe in full the later suicides of Mr. Pupkin, because they were all conducted on the same plan and rested on something the same reasons as above.

Sometimes he would go down at night to the offices of the bank below his bedroom and bring up his bank revolver in order to make an end of himself with it. This, too, he could see headed up in the newspapers as:

BRILLIANT BOY BANKER BLOWS OUT BRAINS

But blowing your brains out is a noisy, rackety performance, and Pupkin soon found that only special kinds of brains are suited for it. So he always sneaked back again later in the night and put the revolver in its place, deciding to drown himself instead. Yet every time that he walked down to the Trestle Bridge over the Ossawippi he found it was quite unsuitable for drowning—too high, and the water too swift and black, and the rushes too gruesome—in fact, not at all the kind of place for a drowning.

Far better, he realized, to wait there on the railroad track and throw himself under the wheels of the express and be done with it. Yet, though Pupkin often waited in this way for the train, he was never able to pick out a pair of wheels that suited him. Anyhow, it's awfully hard to tell an express from a fast freight.

I wouldn't mention these attempts at suicide if one of them hadn't finally culminated in making Peter Pupkin a hero and solving for him the whole perplexed entanglement of his love affair with Zena Pepperleigh. Incidentally it threw him into the very centre of one of the most impenetrable bank mysteries that ever baffled the ingenuity of some of the finest legal talent that ever adorned one of the most enterprising communities in the country.

It happened one night, as I say, that Pupkin decided to go down into the office of the bank and get his revolver and see if it would blow his brains out. It was the night of the Firemen's Ball and Zena had danced four times with a visitor from the city, a man who was in the fourth year at the University and who knew everything. It was more than Peter Pupkin could bear. Mallory Tompkins was away that night, and when Pupkin came home he was all alone in the building, except for Gillis, the caretaker, who lived in the extension at the back.

He sat in his room for hours brooding. Two or three times he picked up a book—he remembered afterwards distinctly that it was Kant's *Critique of Pure Reason*—and tried to read it, but it seemed meaningless and trivial. Then with a sudden access of resolution he started from his chair and made his way down the stairs and into the office room of the bank, meaning to get a revolver and kill himself on the spot and let them find his body lying on the floor.

It was then far on in the night and the empty building of the bank was as still as death. Pupkin could hear the stairs creak under his feet, and as he went he thought he heard another sound like the opening or closing of a door. But it sounded not like the sharp ordinary noise of a closing door but with a dull muffled noise as if someone had shut the iron door of a safe in a room under the ground. For a moment Pupkin stood and listened with his heart thumping against his ribs. Then he kicked his slippers from his feet and without a sound stole into the office on the ground floor and took the revolver from his teller's desk. As he gripped it, he listened to the sounds on the back-stairway and in the vaults below.

I should explain that in the Exchange Bank of Mariposa the offices are on the ground floor level with the street. Below this is another floor with low dark rooms paved with flagstones, with unused office desks and with piles of papers stored in boxes. On this floor are the vaults of the bank, and lying in them in the autumn—the grain season —there is anything from fifty to a hundred thousand dollars in currency tied in bundles. There is no other light down there than the dim reflection from the lights out on the street, that lies in patches on the stone floor.

I think as Peter Pupkin stood, revolver in hand, in the office of the bank, he had forgotten all about the maudlin purpose of his first coming. He had forgotten for the moment all about heroes and love affairs, and his whole mind was focused, sharp and alert, with the intensity of the night-time, on the sounds that he heard in the vault and on the back-stairway of the bank.

Straight away, Pupkin knew what it meant as plainly as if it were written in print. He had forgotten, I say, about being a hero and he only knew that there was sixty thousand dollars in the vault of the bank below, and that he was paid eight hundred dollars a year to look after it.

As Peter Pupkin stood there listening to the sounds in his stockinged feet, his face showed grey as ashes in the light that fell through the window from the street. His heart beat like a hammer against his ribs. But behind its beatings was the blood of four generations of Loyalists, and the robber who would take that sixty thousand dollars from the Mariposa bank must take it over the dead body of Peter Pupkin, teller.

.     .     .     .     .     .     .

Pupkin walked down the stairs to the lower room, the one below the ground with the bank vault in it, with as fine a step as any of his ancestors showed on parade. And if he had known it, as he came down the stairway in the front of the vault room, there was a man crouched in the shadow of the passage way by the stairs at the back. This man, too, held a revolver in his hand, and, criminal or not, his face was as resolute as Pupkin's own. As he heard the teller's step on the stair, he turned and waited in the shadow of the doorway without a sound.

There is no need really to mention all these details. They are only of interest as showing how sometimes a bank teller in a corded smoking jacket and stockinged feet may be turned into such a hero as even the Mariposa girls might dream about.

All of this must have happened at about three o'clock in the night. This much was established afterwards from the evidence of Gillis, the caretaker. When he first heard the sounds he had looked at his watch and noticed that it was half-past two; the watch he knew was three-quarters of an hour slow three days before and had been gaining since.  The exact time at which Gillis heard footsteps in the bank and started downstairs, pistol in hand, became a nice point afterwards in the cross-examination.

But one must not anticipate.  Pupkin reached the iron door of the bank safe, and knelt in front of it, feeling in the dark to find the fracture of the lock.  As he knelt, he heard a sound behind him, and swung around on his knees and saw the bank robber in the half light of the passage way and the glitter of a pistol in his hand.  The rest was over in an instant.  Pupkin heard a voice that was his own, but that sounded strange and hollow, call out: "Drop that, or I'll fire!" and then just as he raised his revolver, there came a blinding flash of light before his eyes, and Peter Pupkin, junior teller of the bank, fell forward on the floor and knew no more.

.    .    .    .    .    .    .

At that point, of course, I ought to close down a chapter, or volume, or, at least, strike the reader over the head with a sandbag to force him to stop and think.  In common fairness one ought to stop here and count a hundred or get up and walk round a block, or, at any rate, picture to oneself Peter Pupkin lying on the floor of the bank, motionless, his arms distended, the revolver still grasped in his hand.  But I must go on.

By half-past seven on the following morning it was known all over Mariposa that Peter Pupkin the junior teller of the Exchange had been shot dead by a bank robber in the vault of the building.  It was known also that Gillis, the caretaker, had been shot and killed at the foot of the stairs, and that the robber had made off with fifty thousand dollars in currency; that he had left a trail of blood on the sidewalk and that the men were out tracking him with bloodhounds in the great swamps to the north of the town.

This, I say, and it is important to note it, was what they knew at half-past seven. Of course as each hour went past they learned more and more. At eight o'clock it was known that Pupkin was not dead, but dangerously wounded in the lungs. At eight-thirty it was known that he was not shot in the lungs, but that the ball had traversed the pit of his stomach.

At nine o'clock it was learned that the pit of Pupkin's stomach was all right, but that the bullet had struck his right ear and carried it away. Finally it was learned that his ear had not exactly been carried away, that is, not precisely removed by the bullet, but that it had grazed Pupkin's head in such a way that it had stunned him, and if it had been an inch or two more to the left it might have reached his brain. This, of course, was just as good as being killed from the point of view of public interest.

Indeed, by nine o'clock Pupkin could be himself seen on the Main Street with a great bandage sideways on his head, pointing out the traces of the robber. Gillis, the caretaker, too, it was known by eight, had not been killed. He had been shot through the brain, but whether the injury was serious or not was only a matter of conjecture. In fact, by ten o'clock it was understood that the bullet from the robber's second shot had grazed the side of the caretaker's head, but as far as could be known his brain was just as before. I should add that the first report about the bloodstains and the swamp and the bloodhounds turned out to be inaccurate. The stains may have been blood, but as they led to the cellar way of Netley's store they may have also been molasses, though it was argued, to be sure, that the robber might well have poured molasses over the bloodstains from sheer cunning.

It was remembered, too, that there were no bloodhounds in Mariposa, although, mind you, there are any amount of dogs there.

So you see that by ten o'clock in the morning the whole affair was settling into the impenetrable mystery which it ever since remained.

Not that there wasn't evidence enough. There was Pupkin's own story and Gillis's story, and the stories of all the people who had heard the shots and seen the robber (some said, the bunch of robbers) go running past (other said, walking past) in the night. Apparently the robber ran up and down half the streets of Mariposa before he vanished.

But the stories of Pupkin and Gillis were plain enough. Pupkin related that he heard sounds in the bank and came downstairs just in time to see the robber crouching in the passage way, and that the robber was a large, hulking, villainous looking man, wearing a heavy coat. Gillis told exactly the same story, having heard the noises at the same time, except that he first described the robber as a small thin fellow (peculiarly villainous looking, however, even in the dark), wearing a short jacket; but on thinking it over, Gillis realized that he had been wrong about the size of the criminal, and that he was even bigger, if anything, than what Mr. Pupkin thought. Gillis had fired at the robber; just at the same moment had Mr. Pupkin.

Beyond that, all was mystery, absolute and impenetrable.

By eleven o'clock the detectives had come up from the city under orders from the head of the bank.

.    .    .    .    .    .    .

I wish you could have seen the two detectives as they moved to and fro in Mariposa—fine looking, stern, impenetrable men that they were. They seemed to take in the whole town by instinct and so quietly. They found their way to Mr. Smith's Hotel just as quietly as if it wasn't design at all and stood there at the bar, picking up scraps of conversation—you know the way detectives do it. Occasionally they allowed one or two bystanders—confederates, perhaps—to buy a drink for them, and you could see from the way they drank it that they were still listening for a clue. If there had been the faintest clue in Smith's Hotel or in the Mariposa House or in the Continental, those fellows would have been at it like a flash.

To see them moving round the town that day—silent, massive, imperturbable—gave one a great idea of their strange, dangerous calling. They went about the town all day and yet in such a quiet peculiar way that you couldn't have realized that they were working at all. They ate their dinner together at Smith's café and took an hour and a half over it to throw people off the scent. Then when they got them off it, they sat and talked with Josh Smith in the back bar to keep them off. Mr. Smith seemed to take to them right away. They were men of his own size, or near it, and anyway hotel men and detectives have a general affinity and share in the same impenetrable silence and in their confidential knowledge of the weaknesses of the public.

Mr. Smith, too, was of great use to the detectives. "Boys," he said, "I wouldn't ask too close as to what folks was out late at night: in this town it don't do."

When those two great brains finally left for the city on the five-thirty, it was hard to realize that behind each grand, impassible face a perfect vortex of clues was seething.

But if the detectives were heroes, what was Pupkin? Imagine him with his bandage on his head standing in front of the bank and talking of the midnight robbery with that peculiar false modesty that only heroes are entitled to use.

I don't know whether you have ever been a hero, but
for sheer exhilaration there is nothing like it.    And for
Mr. Pupkin, who had gone through life thinking himself
no good, to be suddenly exalted into the class of Napoleon
Bonaparte and John Maynard and the Charge of the Light
Brigade—oh, it was wonderful.    Because Pupkin was a
brave man now and he knew it and acquired with it all the
brave man's modesty.    In fact, I believe he was heard to
say that he had only done his duty, and that what he did
was what any other man would have done: though when
somebody else said: "That's so, when you come to think
of it," Pupkin turned on him that quiet look of the
wounded hero, bitterer than words.

And if Pupkin had known that all of the afternoon
papers in the city reported him dead, he would have felt
more luxurious still.

That afternoon the Mariposa court sat in enquiry,—
technically it was summoned in inquest on the dead robber—though they hadn't found the body—and it was
wonderful to see them lining up the witnesses and holding
cross-examinations.    There is something in the cross-examination of great criminal lawyers like Nivens, of Mariposa, and in the counter examinations of presiding judges
like Pepperleigh that thrills you to the core with the
astuteness of it.

They had Henry Mullins, the manager, on the stand
for an hour and a half, and the excitement was so breathless that you could have heard a pin drop.    Nivens took
him on first.

"What is your name?" he said.

"Henry Augustus Mullins."

"What position do you hold?"

"I am manager of the Exchange Bank."

"When were you born?"

"December 30, 1869."

After that, Nivens stood looking quietly at Mullins. You could feel that he was thinking pretty deeply before he shot the next question at him.

"Where did you go to school?"

Mullins answered straight off: "The high school down home," and Nivens thought again for a while and then asked:

"How many boys were at the school?"

"About sixty."

"How many masters?"

"About three."

After that Nivens paused a long while and seemed to be digesting the evidence, but at last an idea seemed to strike him and he said:

"I understand you were not on the bank premises last night. Where were you?"

"Down the lake duck shooting."

You should have seen the excitement in the court when Mullins said this. The judge leaned forward in his chair and broke in at once.

"Did you get any, Harry?" he asked.

"Yes," Mullins said, "about six."

"Where did you get them? What? In the wild rice marsh past the river? You don't say so! Did you get them on the sit or how?"

All of these questions were fired off at the witness from the court in a single breath. In fact, it was the knowledge that the first ducks of the season had been seen in the Ossawippi marsh that led to the termination of the proceedings before the afternoon was a quarter over. Mullins and George Duff and half the witnesses were off with shotguns as soon as the court was cleared.

.     .     .     .     .     .     .     .

I may as well state at once that the full story of the robbery of the bank at Mariposa never came to the light. A number of arrests—mostly of vagrants and suspicious characters—were made, but the guilt of the robbery was never brought home to them. One man was arrested twenty miles away, at the other end of Missinaba county, who not only corresponded exactly with the description of the robber, but, in addition to this, had a wooden leg. Vagrants with one leg are always regarded with suspicion in places like Mariposa, and whenever a robbery or a murder happens they are arrested in batches.

It was never even known just how much money was stolen from the bank. Some people said ten thousand dollars, others more. The bank, no doubt for business motives, claimed that the contents of the safe were intact and that the robber had been foiled in his design.

But none of this matters to the exaltation of Mr. Pupkin. Good fortune, like bad, never comes in small instalments. On that wonderful day, every good thing happened to Peter Pupkin at once. The morning saw him a hero. At the sitting of the court, the judge publicly told him that his conduct was fit to rank among the annals of the pioneers of Tecumseh Township, and asked him to his house for supper. At five o'clock he received the telegram of promotion from the head office that raised his salary to a thousand dollars, and made him not only a hero but a marriageable man. At six o'clock he started up to the judge's house with his resolution nerved to the most momentous step of his life.

His mind was made up.

He would do a thing seldom if ever done in Mariposa. He would propose to Zena Pepperleigh. In Mariposa this kind of step, I say, is seldom taken. The course of love runs on and on through all its stages of tennis playing and dancing and sleigh riding, till by sheer notoriety of circumstance an understanding is reached. To propose straight out would be thought priggish and affected and is supposed to belong only to people in books.

But Pupkin felt that what ordinary people dare not do, heroes are allowed to attempt. He would propose to Zena, and more than that, he would tell her in a straight, manly way that he was rich and take the consequences.

And he did it.

That night on the piazza, where the hammock hangs in the shadow of the Virginia creeper, he did it. By sheer good luck the judge had gone indoors to the library, and by a piece of rare good fortune Mrs. Pepperleigh had gone indoors to the sewing room, and by a happy trick of coincidence the servant was out and the dog was tied up—in fact, no such chain of circumstances was ever offered in favour of mortal man before.

What Zena said—beyond saying yes—I do not know. I am sure that when Pupkin told her of the money, she bore up as bravely as so fine a girl as Zena would, and when he spoke of diamonds she said she would wear them for his sake.

They were saying these things and other things—ever so many other things—when there was such a roar and a clatter up Oneida Street as you never heard, and there came bounding up to the house one of the most marvellous Limousine touring cars that ever drew up at the home of a judge on a modest salary of three thousand dollars. When it stopped there sprang from it an excited man in a long sealskin coat—worn not for the luxury of it at all but from the sheer chilliness of the autumn evening. And it was, as of course you know, Pupkin's father. He had seen the news of his son's death in the evening paper in the city. They drove the car through, so the chauffeur said, in two hours and a quarter, and behind them there was to follow a special trainload of detectives and emergency men, but Pupkin senior had cancelled all that by telegram half way up when he heard that Peter was still living.

For a moment as his eye rested on young Pupkin you would almost have imagined, had you not known that he came from the Maritime Provinces, that there were tears in them and that he was about to hug his son to his heart. But if he didn't hug Peter to his heart, he certainly did within a few moments clasp Zena to it, in that fine fatherly way in which they clasp pretty girls in the Maritime Provinces. The strangest thing is that Pupkin senior seemed to understand the whole situation without any explanations at all.

Judge Pepperleigh, I think, would have shaken both of Pupkin senior's arms off when he saw him; and when you heard them call one another "Ned" and "Phillip" it made you feel that they were boys again attending classes together at the old law school in the city.

If Pupkin thought that his father wouldn't make a hit in Mariposa, it only showed his ignorance. Pupkin senior sat there on the judge's verandah smoking a corn cob pipe as if he had never heard of Havana cigars in his life. In the three days that he spent in Mariposa that autumn, he went in and out of Jeff Thorpe's barber shop and Eliot's drug store, shot black ducks in the marsh and played poker every evening at a hundred matches for a cent as if he had never lived any other life in all his days. They had to send him telegrams enough to fill a satchel to make him come away.

So Pupkin and Zena in due course of time were married, and went to live in one of the enchanted houses on the hillside in the newer part of the town, where you may find them to this day.

You may see Pupkin there at any time cutting enchanted grass on a little lawn in as gaudy a blazer as ever.

But if you step up to speak to him or walk with him into the enchanted house, pray modulate your voice a little —musical though it is—for there is said to be an enchanted baby on the premises whose sleep must not lightly be disturbed.

# The Sit-Down Strike in My Parlour

*They Came and They Wouldn't Go*

THE sit-down strikers—who sat down the other night in my living-room—had timed their arrival with characteristic cunning. They came just after dark, between eight and nine in the evening. All six arrived in one motor car so as to effect a quick and immediate entry before anyone could stop them. With proper warning I could easily have prevented an entry. My plant is a large country house with a lodge and driveway, and protected in the rear by a lake. A heavy chain stretched across the drive could have brought the car to a stop. As it was, nothing was done. No chain was placed and there was no tear-gas in the house.

The result was that they were in, had slipped past the maid at the door, thrown off all their graps and had occupied the living-room before any organized attempt could be made to eject them.

It was there that I was summoned for a conference. They appeared to be, as I said, six—two men and two women, evidently husbands and wives, and two younger criminals, a grown-up girl and boy, quite old enough to be held legally responsible.

Now here began the difficulty. People who only know of sit-down strikes from hearsay, as I am afraid is the case with even some of our judges, cannot estimate the practical difficulty of dealing with the strikers. But any plant manager will understand my case. An outsider would ask, "Why not throw them all out? Your plant," he would say, "is your property. These sit-down people are just trespassers." True, but you see I *knew* them; they were people that I knew, just as the plant manager knows and has worked for years with the leaders of his strike. Apart from their presence in my plant, I had nothing against them. One of our judges asked the other day, "Why not throw them out by the neck?" Well, these two senior women were in evening dress and were of the solid kind that has no neck.

They opened the discussion, cleverly enough, by drawing attention to the fine spring weather; I admitted that it was fine but claimed that it still turned bitter cold later at night. They denied this flat out. Then I made my first, tentative offer, viz., that they must have a whiskey and soda or ginger ale with ice, a choice, before they left. They agreed, but without clause two. For the time being I was beaten, but it occurred to me that in getting ice for the drinks I might make some use of the telephone to get them home. The younger criminal frustrated this by coming to help me. While getting the ice he put in an ingenious claim that he had been a student of mine in Economics when I was a professor. There was no way to challenge this. He may have been. A lot of my students went to the bad.

When I got back to the living-room the sit-downers had settled in to their task and were well ensconced round the fire, which they stirred to a blaze. They came out boldly with their first demand and suggested a game of bridge. I urged that I had no cards. But their preliminary organization had provided this. It seemed that one of the women strikers had cards in her bag.

By ten o'clock the sit-down strike was in full operation. The strikers were playing bridge, four at a time, with two as pickets to keep their eye on me. The system I believe is called "cutting-in" and is largely used in cases like this where a sit-down strike is carried on in a private dwelling.

Of bridge I know nothing, but it was clear that we had reached a rough and ready understanding, namely, that they would play without further annoyance to the property provided that I kept up the fire and supplied whiskey and soda after each rubber.    For those not conversant with bridge I may say that a "rubber" is the name given to the period between drinks.

The sit-down strikers were thus getting about fifty cents an hour, which they raised to sixty cents an hour after eleven o'clock by working shorter rubbers.    I had to give in.    One man made a distinct threat that, if I didn't, they'd stay all night.    What he said was, "I just feel as if I could play all night!" but I knew what he *meant*.    And when one woman went over to the piano and hit a couple of notes, and sang, "We won't go home till morning!" I knew that they might start violence at any time.

I repeat again that people who only think in terms of theory fail to realize how difficult it is in practice to fight against sit-down strikers.    They would say, "Why didn't you get one and use force, attack him, kill him!"    I tried to.    I got one of the men strikers, while he was picketing, and took him down to the cellar under pretense of fixing the furnace, but he artfully kept out of reach of the shovel.    Then I took him on the lawn to look at the lake, but I couldn't get him near enough.

So when we came in I made a flat out offer of seventy-five cents' worth of whiskey and a plate of sandwiches if they'd go—that is, before they went.    But it only led to a lot of back and forward discussion.    One woman said: "Oh, yes, sandwiches would be lovely!    *Do* let's stop a minute!"    But the other said: "No, Mary, we don't need to stop.    We can eat the sandwiches right here."

After that, it was nearly one in the morning, I gave right in. I knew there was a cold turkey in the ice-box, the real thing—plump and cool and lying all dressed up with green parsley. Show that to a woman of the make and build that these were, and you've got her.

I beat them with that. Within ten minutes I had them round the dining-room table with the turkey; they had found half a cold ham and a few other things and claimed the lot. We were acting on a fair and square "gentleman's agreement" that they'd eat all they could and then go. There was a little murmuring; indeed someone suggested a round of cold hands at poker or something, and one woman said that when she got going she could go on all night. But there was a general feeling that my offer was a fair compromise, and they took it.

They made *one* stipulation however. They are all coming back next Tuesday, and they are going to bring two others with them, visitors who are coming up from Cincinnati. They say that these are "lovely people." I don't doubt it. And they say that they are just dying to meet me. All right. Let them die.

Next Tuesday I'll be ready. The chain will be across the drive. John Kelly, my lodge-keeper, a determined man who has seen something of Sinn Fein Ireland, is a handy man with bird-shot. And I ordered ten gallons of tear-gas.

.    .    .    .    .    .    .

And yet—oh, I don't know—somehow you just can't! That's the bother with the sit-down strikes in social life. They'll come and I'll let them in, and they'll say, "Well! here we are again!" and one of the women will get off that old thing about the bad penny, and then say, "I want you to meet Mr. and Mrs. Potzenjammer of Cincinnati," and I'll say, "What about a little Scotch?"

All right. Life is just repetition.

# When Men Retire

My old friend Mr. McPherson retired from the flour and feed business—oh, quite a few years ago. He said it was time to get out and give young Charlie a chance—even then "young Charlie" was getting near fifty. Anyway old Mr. McPherson said he wasn't going to keep his nose to the grindstone for ever.

I don't mean that he absolutely dropped out of the business; but, as he himself said, he took it easy. The McPhersons had a fine business, two or three big mills and a central office in our home town. Always, before he retired, Mr. McPherson would be down at the office sharp at eight—the flour and feed is an early business. When he retired he gave all that up. He'd loaf in anywhere round ten minutes past, or sometimes even twenty. It was the same way after lunch—or at least I mean after "dinner"; they don't have "lunch" in the flour and feed business; they have dinner at noon. After dinner if Mr. McPherson didn't feel like getting up and walking to the office at one o'clock, he'd drive down in a cab. And at five o'clock, when the office closed, if he didn't feel like going home right away, he'd stay for a while and run over some of the day's invoices. Or perhaps, if he felt like it, he'd go over to the mill, because the mill didn't close till six, and just fool around there a while helping the men bag up some of the farmers' orders.

One thing, though, that Mr. McPherson insists on, now that he's retired, is that, as he himself says, he never interferes. The business, as he explains, belongs now to the children. That means young Charlie and Lavinia—bless me! Lavinia must be not far from sixty; she keeps the house. To those two and a married daughter in Scotland. The old man has never transferred the business in any legal sense. He says it isn't necessary as long as he's alive. But it's *theirs* just the same, and he tells them so. And, as I say, he doesn't interfere; "young Charlie" is the general manager, and all his father does is just to look over the contracts to see what's doing, and keep an eye on the produce market to advise young Charlie when to buy —but only, mind you, to advise.

What's more, as Mr. McPherson himself loves to explain, he's not like a man who can't cut loose from business and enjoy himself. Oh, my no! Every year there's the St. Andrews dinner in the Odd Fellows' Hall, regular as clock-work, and every year Burns' birthday, when a few of them get together and have a big old time and read Burns out loud. And only four years ago Mr. McPherson took a trip to Scotland and saw his married daughter and Burns' grave and the big flour mills at Dumbarton, and paid for it all out of a commission on No. 1 wheat. Oh, no, Mr. McPherson says he never regrets his retirement: he can't think what it would be like to be back in harness.

. . . . . . .

My friend McAlpin was a banker—assistant general manager of a bank. He retired in the natural, normal course of things in accordance with the bank regulations. He made no plan or preparation for retirement. He said that it was enough for him to be rid of the strain of work. He'd have his mind free. So he would have had, if it hadn't happened that, on his first morning of retirement, as he walked down town, he felt a sort of wheeziness, a kind of, well, not exactly a pain, but a sort of compression. Anyway, a druggist gave him some bicarbonate of bismuth —he's told me about it himself ever so many times—or

was it bisulphate of something?    Anyway it fixed Mc-
Alpin up all right but it left him with a sort of feeling
of flatulence, or flobbulence (he's explained it to me) that
bothered him all morning till a friend told him to drink
Vichy water, two or three quarts at a time.    Now as a
matter of fact you see McAlpin had had that wheeziness
every morning for years back when he went to the bank.
But as soon as he opened the mail and began dictating, the
wheeziness vanished, and the flobbulence never started.
But the moment he retired, the wheeziness brought on the
flobbulence; and Vichy water is all right, but there's so
much chalk in it that if you take it you must follow it
with an anticalcide of some sort.    I don't know the names,
but McAlpin has told me about them—bigusphate of car-
bon or any other antiscorbutic.

In fact, as McAlpin tells me, he has come to realize
that his diet while he was in the bank was all wrong.    He
used to take bacon and eggs for breakfast, whereas now
that he has looked into things he finds that bacon has no
food value at all—contains no postulates.    Eggs would be
all right if taken with a germicide, but they lack vitamins.
So what McAlpin eats now—he tells me this himself—is a
proper balance of protein and carbohydrates.

McAlpin spends a good deal of his time in the drug
stores.    He says those fellows know a lot.    Do you realize
that if you take a drink of mineral water every half hour,
with a touch of salt in it, it keeps your sebaceous glands
open?

When McAlpin takes a holiday he goes down to Nugget
Springs where the thermal baths are.    It's a new place and
he says that they say that the doctors say that the water
has a lower alkali content than any other.    That's why
he goes there, for the low alkali content.    You take a bath
every hour and in between you drink the water and the

rest of the time you sit in it. McAlpin says that when he comes back he feels a hundred per cent more crustaceous than he did before. He attributes this to phosphorus.

. . . . . . .

My friend Tharpe, who was in Iron and Steel, retired to Paris. He retired at fifty-eight. He said he wanted to retire while he was still fresh enough to enjoy life—feel those muscles. He wanted to have a little fun in life, before he sank into old age. So he went over to Paris to have, as he himself so fervently put it, "a whale of a time."

I saw him there six months later, in a night-supper restaurant. He had with him something that looked like an odelisk—isn't that the word?—anyway something Moorish with slanting eyes and a crescent diadem. Tharpe came over and spoke to me. He looked like a boiled lobster, all red and black. He said he felt fine. He said he was just starting out for the evening. He felt, he said, A.1.

I saw him in the hotel next morning. He was in the barber shop. The barber was fixing him up. He looked about four colors, mostly black and yellow. He said he felt great. The barber was steaming him, boiling him and squirting things over him. Then he went up to the drug store and the druggist "fixed him"—washed him right out —and then into the bar and the bartender "fixed him"—toned him right up with a couple of "eye-openers." Then he started off. He had on a pongee suit and a panama hat and a French silk tie, and he looked pretty slick, but battered. He said he felt fine. He said he was going out to play baccarat with two men he met the night before—Russians—he couldn't remember their names—Sonovitch or Dombroski or something. Anyway one of them was a cousin of the Czar. He said he felt elegant.

Tharpe is in a home just now, in England—a rest home. He's taking the rest cure, and then he is to take the gold cure and after that a brain cure. A big English doctor took out part of his skull. He says he feels A.1. He has lost most of his money and he's coming back to the Iron and Steel business. He says it beats Paris.

·    ·    ·    ·    ·    ·    ·

A peculiarly interesting case of retirement has been that of my long-time friend the Senior Professor of Greek at the college here. When he retired the Chancellor of the University said at the Convocation that our regret at Professor Dim's retirement was tempered by the fact that we realized that he would now be able to complete the studies on Homer's *Odyssey* which had occupied him for so many years. Notice, to *complete*. The general supposition was that in all these long years, in all the evenings of his spare time he'd been working on Homer's *Odyssey*, and that now all that he needed was a little time and breathing space and the brilliant studies would be consolidated into a book. To *complete*—and I was the only one who knew that he hadn't even started. He had begun, ever so many years ago, when we were fellow juniors, talking of Homer's *Odyssey*. There was something he wanted to do about it —I forget just what; either to prove that there was never any Homer or that there was never any Odyssey. At any rate it was one of those big academic problems that professors select as a life work. It began to be understood that he was "working on Homer's *Odyssey*"; then that he was doing a book on Homer's *Odyssey*, and then that he had nearly done it, and only needed time to *complete* it. And all the time he hadn't started. Professors are like that.

·    ·    ·    ·    ·    ·    ·

The years go by so easily—Commencement Day and a new session—you can't begin anything then—mid-session, impossible—final exams and the end of the session—out of the question to start anything then; a man must rest sometime. And you don't start Homer in the long vacation on the coast of Maine.

So when Professor Dim retired, people on the street would stop him and ask, "How's the book coming on?" And he could only turn pink and gurgle something. I'm the only one who knows that he hasn't started it. He's been getting pretty frail the last two winters; some of his old pupils sent him south last winter, so that he could finish his book. He didn't. They gave him a trip up north last summer—but not far enough. They talk now of sending him to Greece where the *Odyssey* began. They're afraid, some of them—this, of course, they say very gently and kindly—they're afraid that the old fellow may not live to finish the book. I know that he won't. He hasn't started.

But as to this retirement business, let me give a word of advice to all of you young fellows round fifty. Some of you have been talking of it and even looking forward to it. Have nothing to do with it. Listen; it's like this. Have you ever been out for a late autumn walk in the closing part of the afternoon, and suddenly looked up to realize that the leaves have practically all gone? You hadn't realized it. And you notice that the sun has set already, the day gone before you knew it—and with that a cold wind blows across the landscape. That's retirement.

# This Strenuous Age

SOMETHING is happening, I regret to find, to the world in which we used to live. The poor old thing is being "speeded up." There is "efficiency" in the air. Offices open at eight o'clock. Millionaires lunch on a baked apple. Bankers eat practically nothing. A college president has declared that there are more foot pounds of energy in a glass of peptonized milk than in—something else, I forget what. All this is very fine. Yet somehow I feel out of it.

My friends are failing me. They won't sit up after midnight. They have taken to sleeping out of doors, on porches and pergolas. Some, I understand, merely roost on plain wooden bars. They rise early. They take deep breathing. They bathe in ice water. They are no good.

This change, I am sure, is excellent. It is, I am certain, just as it ought to be. I am merely saying, quietly and humbly, that I am not in it. I am being left behind. Take, for example, the case of alcohol. That, at least, is what it is called now. There were days when we called it Bourbon whiskey and Tom Gin, and when the very name of it breathed romance. That time is past.

The poor stuff is now called alcohol, and none so low that he has a good word for it. Quite right, I am certain. I don't defend it. Alcohol, they are saying to-day, if taken in sufficient quantities, tears all the outer coating off the diaphragm. It leaves the epigastric tissue, so I am informed, a useless wreck.

This I don't deny. It gets, they tell me, into the brain. I don't dispute it. It turns the prosencephalon into mere punk. I know it. I've felt it doing it. They tell me—

and I believe it—that after even one glass of alcohol, or shall we say Scotch whiskey and soda, a man's working power is lowered by twenty per cent. This is a dreadful thing. After three glasses, so it is held, his capacity for sustained rigid thought is cut in two. And after about six glasses the man's working power is reduced by at least a hundred per cent. He merely sits there—in his armchair, at his club, let us say, with all power, even all *desire* to work gone out of him, not thinking rigidly, not sustaining his thought, a mere shapeless chunk of geniality, half hidden in the blue smoke of his cigar.

Very dreadful, not a doubt. Alcohol is doomed; it is going; it is gone. Yet when I think of a hot Scotch on a winter evening, or a Tom Collins on a summer morning, or a gin rickey beside a tennis court, or a stein of beer on a bench beside a bowling green—I wish somehow that we could prohibit the use of alcohol and merely drink beer and whiskey and gin as we used to. But these things, it appears, interfere with work. They have got to go.

But turn to the broader and simpler question of WORK itself. In my time one hated it. It was viewed as the natural enemy of man. Now the world has fallen in love with it. My friends, I find, take their deep breathing and their porch sleeping because it makes them work better. They go for a week's vacation in Virginia not for its own sake, but because they say they can work better when they get back. I know a man who wears very loose boots because he can work better in them: and another who wears only soft shirts because he can work better in a soft shirt. There are plenty of men now who would wear dog-harness if they thought they could work more in it. I know another man who walks away out into the country every Sunday: not that he likes the country: he wouldn't recognize a bumblebee if he saw it: but he claims that if he walks on Sunday his head is as clear as a bell for work on Monday.

Against work itself, I say nothing. But I sometimes wonder if I stand alone in this thing. Am I the *only* person left who hates it?

Nor is work all. Take food. I admit, here and now, that the lunch I like best—I mean for an ordinary plain lunch, not a party—is a beefsteak about one foot square and two inches thick. Can I work on it? No, I can't, but I can work in spite of it. That is as much as one used to ask, twenty-five years ago.

Yet now I find that all my friends boast ostentatiously about the meagre lunch they eat. One tells me that he finds a glass of milk and a prune is quite as much as he cares to take. Another says that a dry biscuit and a glass of water is all that his brain will stand. One lunches on the white of an egg. Another eats merely the yolk. I have only two friends left who can eat a whole egg at a time.

I understand that the fear of these men is that if they eat more than an egg or a biscuit, they will feel heavy after lunch. Why they object to feeling heavy, I do not know. Personally, I enjoy it. I like nothing better than to sit round after a heavy lunch with half a dozen heavy friends, smoking heavy cigars. I am well aware that that is wicked. I merely confess the fact. I do not palliate it.

Nor is food all, nor drink, nor work, nor open air. There has spread abroad along with the so-called physical efficiency a perfect passion for *information*. Somehow if a man's stomach is empty and his head clear as a bell, and if he won't drink and won't smoke, he reaches out for information. He wants facts. He reads the newspapers all through, instead of only reading the headings. He clamours for articles filled with statistics about illiteracy and alien immigration and the number of battleships in the Japanese navy.

I know quite a lot of men who have actually bought the new Encyclopædia Britannica. What is more, they *read* the thing. They sit in their apartments at night with a glass of water at their elbow reading the encyclopædia. They say that it is literally filled with facts. Other men spend their time reading the Statistical Abstract of the United States (they say the figures in it are great) and the Acts of Congress, and the list of Presidents since Washington (or was it Washington?).

Spending their evenings thus, and topping it off with a cold baked apple, and sleeping out in the snow, they go to work in the morning, so they tell me, with a positive sense of exhilaration. I have no doubt that they do. But for me, I confess that once and for all I am out of it. I am left behind.

Add to it all such rising dangers as total prohibition, and the female franchise, the daylight saving, and eugenic marriage, together with proportional representation, the initiative and the referendum, and the duty of the citizen to take an intelligent interest in politics—and I admit that I shall not be sorry to go away from here.

But before I *do* go, I have one hope. I understand that down in Hayti things are very different. Bull fights, cock fights, dog fights, are openly permitted. Business never begins till eleven in the morning. Everybody sleeps after lunch, and the bars remain open all night. Marriage is but a casual relation. In fact, the general condition of morality, so they tell me, is lower in Hayti than it has been anywhere since the time of Nero. Me for Hayti.

# How I Succeeded in My Business

*Secrets of Success as Related in the*
*Best Current Literature*

I HAD been employed in one business and another quite a good few years, more years than I cared to look back upon; and yet I hadn't made good. I hadn't made good, and I knew I hadn't made good, and sometimes the knowledge that I hadn't made good made me feel bad. Often I said to my wife when I came home nights, "Doll," I said, "I haven't made good." "No, Jim, old boy," she'd say, "I know you haven't made good, but never mind you'll make good yet." And then I'd see a tear fall from her eye on to the dresser. After that I'd go out and sit in the back yard and feel real bad.

Often I used to think it over as to why it was I hadn't made good. I'd had about as much education as most, and more experience than many and better chances than some. I was willing enough and steady enough. I was a non-drinker and a non-smoker; I never touched a card and had never seen a horse race in my life, and never been inside the doors of a pool-room. Yet I knew as well as anybody just where my shortcomings were; I lacked pep, I had no punch, I had practically no magnetism, and I didn't react quickly on a given environment. And I knew that now-a-days in business it is magnetism and pep and reaction that make for success. Then, too, I failed in the little things; I couldn't add up more than one column of figures at a time and my memory was no good: things seemed to slip out of it. Often when I came home of an

club. There was a big bill of fare, but I took no meat at all, only half a bucket of spinach. I noticed that Mr. Kitson ate nothing but boiled water-cress.

"Now, Jim," said Mr. Kitson, "I've had my eye on you all the morning, and I believe you're the man we want. The company wants someone to go to Kansas City to line up a man and to swing a big proposition."

"Mr. Kitson," I interrupted, "I can line him up and swing it."

"When can you go?"

"Right now," I said, "as soon as I finish my spinach. Just tell me what it is that I swing when I get there."

"Good!" he said. "The man that you are to see is John Smith of John Street. Can you remember the name? Better write it down."

"I don't need to," I said. "Just say the name over three or four times and my memory will take a grip on it. I'll take a few deep breaths while you say it."

So I went right over to the house and packed my grip.

"Doll," I said, "I'm off to Kansas City."

"What to do?" Doll asked.

"To swing a proposition," I answered. "It's a big thing, Doll, with big people, and if I make good we'll come out big."

I left on the cars that night, and all the way out I ate grass and cultivated my memory and reacted all the time on everything I saw.

Well, when I got to Kansas City, I found I was up against something pretty big, all right. I found John Smith but he wouldn't see me. I went right into his office, and I said, "Mr. Smith, can I see you?" "No," he said, "you can't." However, I hung on. "Let me see you," I said. "No, I won't," he answered. Still I wouldn't give in. I went up to his house that evening and right into his library. "Can I see you now?" I asked. "No," he answered, "you can't see me." "Look here! Mr. Smith," I pleaded, "I've come two thousand miles to see you: let me see you!" "No, Dudley," he said, "I won't."

That went on four days and at last he gave in. "All right, Jim," he said, "state your business. What do you want?" "I want to line you up—swing you," I said, "come out with me, Mr. Smith, and eat spinach, and I'll tell you about it."

So I took him out to a swell restaurant where they had the best spinach in Kansas City. "Now," I said after we had eaten, "you're a big man and this is a big thing: we want to put over something pretty big and you're the man we want in on it. You're big."

"Jim," he said, "you talk well. And what's more, you've got personality and that's the biggest thing in business to-day. As soon as I see a man who has personality, I do whatever he wants. Personality gets me every time."

So I got what I wanted, and I took the train right back to New York. Doll met me at the depot. I kissed her right there on the platform. "Did you swing it?" she asked. "Yes, Doll, I did," I answered. I saw Doll drop a tear right on the platform. "Good old Jim," she said.

Next morning I found an envelope on my desk with a cheque for five thousand dollars in it.

Well, that was how I got my first start. Once the firm found that I could line up a man and swing a thing of that size there was lots more for me to do. So the end of it was they made me the head of the company. "It's no use trying to keep you down, Jim," said Mr. Kitson. "You're the biggest of all of us."

So I went home to Doll and I said, "Doll," I said, "I'm made president of the company." "Oh, Jim!" she said, "you've made good. I'm so proud—and I'm proud of the company, too, now that you're president of it. So you must tell me all about it, what it does and what it makes and sells."

"Doll," I answered, "don't ask me. I've been so busy swinging propositions and lining things up and breathing and eating spinach, that I've never had time to find out what on earth the company does do."

# Winsome Winnie: or, Trial and Temptation

## THROWN ON THE WORLD

"Miss Winnifred," said the Old Lawyer, looking keenly over and through his shaggy eyebrows at the fair young creature seated before him, "you are this morning twenty-one."

Winnifred Clair raised her deep mourning veil, lowered her eyes and folded her hands.

"This morning," continued Mr. Bonehead, "my guardianship is at an end."

There was a tone of something like emotion in the voice of the stern old lawyer, while for a moment his eye glistened with something like a tear which he hastened to remove with something like a handkerchief. "I have therefore sent for you," he went on, "to render you an account of my trust."

He heaved a sigh at her, and then reaching out his hand he pulled the woollen bell rope up and down several times.

An aged clerk appeared.

"Did the bell ring?" he asked.

"I think it did," said the lawyer. "Be good enough, Atkinson, to fetch me the papers of the estate of the late Major Clair defunct."

"I have them here," said the clerk, and he laid upon the table a bundle of faded blue papers, and withdrew.

"Miss Winnifred," resumed the Old Lawyer, "I will now proceed to give you an account of the disposition that has been made of your property. This first document refers to the sum of two thousand pounds left to you by your great uncle. It is lost."

Winnifred bowed.

"Pray give me your best attention and I will endeavour to explain to you how I lost it."

"Oh, sir!" cried Winnifred, "I am only a poor girl unskilled in the ways of the world and knowing nothing but music and French, I fear that the details of business are beyond my grasp. But if it is lost, I gather that it is gone."

"It is," said Mr. Bonehead. "I lost it in a marginal option in an undeveloped oil company. I suppose that means nothing to you."

"Alas," sighed Winnifred, "nothing."

"Very good," resumed the lawyer. "Here next we have a statement in regard to the thousand pounds left you under the will of your maternal grandmother. I lost it at Monte Carlo. But I need not fatigue you with the details."

"Pray spare them," cried the girl.

"This final item relates to the sum of fifteen hundred pounds placed in trust for you by your uncle. I lost it on a horse race. That horse," added the Old Lawyer with rising excitement, "ought to have won. He was coming down the stretch like blue—but there, there, my dear, you must forgive me if the recollection of it still stirs me to anger. Suffice it to say the horse fell. I have kept for your inspection the score card of the race, and the betting tickets. You will find everything in order."

"Sir," said Winnifred, as Mr. Bonehead proceeded to fold up his papers, "I am but a poor inadequate girl, a mere child in business, but tell me I pray what is left to me of the money that you have managed?"

"Nothing," said the lawyer. "Everything is gone. And I regret to say Miss Clair that it is my painful duty to convey to you a further disclosure of a distressing nature. It concerns your birth."

"Just Heaven!" cried Winnifred, with a woman's quick intuition. "Does it concern my father?"

"It does, Miss Clair. Your father was not your father."

"Oh, sir," exclaimed Winnifred. "My poor mother! How she must have suffered!"

"Your mother was not your mother," said the Old Lawyer, gravely. "Nay, nay, do not question me. There is a dark secret about your birth."

"Alas," said Winnifred, wringing her hands, "I am, then, alone in the world and penniless."

"You are," said Mr. Bonehead, deeply moved. "You are, unfortunately, thrown upon the world. But if you ever find yourself in a position where you need help and advice, do not scruple to come to me. Especially," he added, "for advice."

"And meantime let me ask you in what way do you propose to earn your livelihood?"

"I have my needle," said Winnifred.

"Let me see it," said the lawyer.

Winnifred showed it to him.

"I fear," said Mr. Bonehead, shaking his head, "you will not do much with that."

Then he rang the bell again.

"Atkinson," he said, "take Miss Clair out and throw her on the world."

## II

### A RENCOUNTER

As Winnifred Clair passed down the stairway leading from the lawyer's office, a figure appeared before her in the corridor blocking the way. It was that of a tall aristocratic-looking man whose features wore that peculiarly saturnine appearance seen only in the English nobility. The face, while entirely gentlemanly in its general aspect, was stamped with all the worst passions of mankind.

Had the innocent girl but known it, the face was that of Lord Wynchgate, one of the most contemptible of the greater nobility of Britain, and the figure was his too.

"Ha!" exclaimed the dissolute Aristocrat, "whom have we here! Stay, pretty one, and let me see the fair countenance that I divine behind your veil."

"Sir!" said Winnifred, drawing herself up proudly, "let me pass, I pray."

"Not so," cried Wynchgate, reaching out and seizing his intended victim by the wrist, "not till I have at least seen the colour of those eyes and imprinted a kiss upon those fair lips."

With a brutal laugh, he drew the struggling girl towards him.

In another moment the aristocratic villain would have succeeded in lifting the veil of the unhappy girl, when suddenly a ringing voice cried, "Hold! stop! desist! begone! lay to! cut it out!"

With these words a tall athletic young man, attracted doubtless by the girl's cries, leapt into the corridor from the street without. His figure was that, more or less, of a Greek god, while his face, although at the moment inflamed with anger, was of an entirely moral and permissible configuration.

"Save me! save me!" cried Winnifred.

"I will," cried the Stranger, rushing towards Lord Wynchgate with uplifted cane.

But the cowardly Aristocrat did not await the onslaught of the unknown.

"You shall yet be mine!" he hissed in Winnifred's ear, and releasing his grasp, he rushed with a bound past the rescuer into the street.

"Oh, sir!" said Winnifred, clasping her hands and falling on her knees in gratitude. "I am only a poor inadequate girl, but if the prayers of one, who can offer naught but her prayers to her benefactor, can avail to the advantage of one who appears to have every conceivable advantage already, let him know that they are his."

"Nay," said the Stranger, as he aided the blushing girl to rise, "kneel not to me, I beseech. If I have done aught to deserve the gratitude of one who, whoever she is, will remain forever present as a bright memory in the breast of one in whose breast such memories are all too few, he is all too richly repaid. If she does that, he is blessed indeed."

"She does. He is!" cried Winnifred, deeply moved. "Here on her knees she blesses him. And now," she added, "we must part. Seek not to follow me. One who has aided a poor girl in the hour of need will respect her wish when she tells him that, alone and buffeted by the world, her one prayer is that he will leave her."

"He will!" cried the Unknown. "He will. He does."

"Leave me, yes, leave me," exclaimed Winnifred.

"I will," said the Unknown.

"Do, do," sobbed the distraught girl. "Yet stay, one

moment more. Let she, who has received so much from her benefactor, at least know his name."

"He cannot! He must not!" exclaimed the Indistinguishable. "His birth is such—but enough!"

He tore his hand from the girl's detaining clasp and rushed forth from the place.

Winnifred Clair was alone.

III

FRIENDS IN DISTRESS

Winnifred was now in the humblest lodgings in the humblest part of London. A simple bedroom and sitting room sufficed for her wants. Here she sat on her trunk, bravely planning for the future.

"Miss Clair," said the landlady, knocking at the door, "do try to eat something. You must keep your health. See, I've brought you a kippered herring."

Winnifred ate the herring, her heart filled with gratitude. With renewed strength she sallied forth on the street to resume her vain search for employment. For two weeks now Winnifred Clair had sought employment even of the humblest character. At various dressmaking establishments she had offered, to no purpose, the services of her needle. They had looked at it and refused it.

In vain she had offered to various editors and publishers the use of her pen. They had examined it coldly and refused it.

She had tried fruitlessly to obtain a position of trust. The various banks and trust companies to which she had applied declined her services. In vain she had advertised in the newspapers offering to take sole charge of a little girl. No one would give her one.

Her slender stock of money which she had in her purse on leaving Mr. Bonehead's office was almost consumed.

Each night the unhappy girl returned to her lodging exhausted with disappointment and fatigue.

Yet even in her adversity she was not altogether friendless.

Each evening on her return home, a soft tap was heard at the door.

"Miss Clair," said the voice of the landlady, "I have brought you a fried egg. Eat it. You must keep up your strength."

Then one morning a terrible temptation had risen before her.

"Miss Clair," said the manager of an agency to which she had applied, "I am glad to be able at last to make you a definite offer of employment. Are you prepared to go upon the stage?"

The stage!

A flush of shame and indignation swept over the girl. Had it come to this? Little versed in the world as Winnifred was, she knew but too well the horror, the iniquity, the depth of degradation implied in the word.

"Yes," continued the agent, "I have a letter here asking me to recommend a young lady of suitable refinement to play the part of Eliza in Uncle Tom's Cabin. Will you accept?"

"Sir," said Winnifred proudly, "answer me first this question fairly. If I go upon the stage, can I, as Eliza, remain as innocent, as simple as I am now?"

"You can not," said the manager.

"Then, sir," said Winnifred, rising from her chair, "let me say this. Your offer is doubtless intended to be kind. Coming from the class you do and inspired by the ideas you are, you no doubt mean well. But let a poor girl, friendless and alone, tell you that rather than accept such a degradation she will die."

"Very good," said the manager.

"I go forth," cried Winnifred, "to perish."

"All right," said the manager.

The door closed behind her. Winnifred Clair, once more upon the street, sank down upon the steps of the building in a swoon.

But at this very juncture Providence, which always watches over the innocent and defenceless, was keeping its eye direct upon Winnifred.

At that very moment when our heroine sank fainting upon the doorstep, a handsome equipage drawn by two superb black steeds happened to pass along the street.

Its appearance and character proclaimed it at once to be one of those vehicles in which only the superior classes of the exclusive aristocracy are privileged to ride. Its sides were emblazoned with escutcheons, insignia and other paraphernalia. The large gilt coronet that appeared upon its panelling surmounted by a bunch of huckleberries, quartered in a field of potatoes, indicated that its possessor was, at least, of the rank of marquis. A coachman and two grooms rode in front, while two footmen seated in the boot, or box at the rear, contrived, by the immobility of their attitude and the melancholy of their faces, to inspire the scene with an exclusive and aristocratic grandeur.

The occupants of the equipage—for we refuse to count the menials as being such—were two in number, a lady and gentleman, both of advancing years. Their snow-white hair and benign countenances indicated that they belonged to that rare class of beings to whom rank and wealth are but an incentive to nobler things. A gentle philanthropy played all over their faces, and their eyes sought eagerly in the passing scene of the humble street for new objects of benefaction.

Those acquainted with the countenances of the aristocracy would have recognized at once in the occupants of the equipage the Marquis of Muddlenut and his spouse, the Marchioness.

It was the eye of the Marchioness which first detected the form of Winnifred Clair upon the doorstep.

"Hold! pause! stop!" she cried, in lively agitation.

The horses were at once pulled in, the brakes applied to the wheels, and with the aid of a powerful lever, operated by three of the menials the carriage was brought to a standstill.

"See!  Look!" cried the Marchioness.  "She has fainted. Quick, William, your flask.  Let us hasten to her aid."

In another moment the noble lady was bending over the prostrate form of Winnifred Clair, and pouring brandy between her lips.

Winnifred opened her eyes.  "Where am I?" she asked feebly.

"She speaks!" cried the Marchioness.  "Give her another flaskful."

After the second flask the girl sat up.

"Tell me," she cried, clasping her hands, "what has happened?  Where am I?"

"With friends!" answered the Marchioness.  "But do not essay to speak.  Drink this.  You must husband your strength.  Meantime, let us drive you to your home."

Winnifred was lifted tenderly by the men-servants into the aristocratic equipage.  The brake was unset, the lever reversed, and the carriage thrown again into motion.

On the way Winnifred, at the solicitation of the Marchioness, related her story.

"My poor child," exclaimed the lady, "how you must

have suffered. Thank Heaven it is over now. Tomorrow we shall call for you and bring you away with us to Muddlenut Chase."

Alas! could she but have known it, before the morrow should dawn, worse dangers still were in store for our heroine. But what these dangers were, we must reserve for another chapter.

IV

### A GAMBLING PARTY IN ST. JAMES'S CLOSE

We must now ask our readers to shift the scene—if they don't mind doing this for us—to the apartments of the Earl of Wynchgate in St. James's Close. The hour is nine o'clock in the evening, and the picture before us is one of revelry and dissipation so characteristic of the nobility of England. The atmosphere of the room is thick with blue Havana smoke such as is used by the nobility, while on the green baize table a litter of counters and cards in which aces, kings, and even two spots are heaped in confusion, proclaim the reckless nature of the play.

Seated about the table are six men dressed in the height of fashion, each with collar and white necktie and broad white shirt, their faces stamped with all, or nearly all, of the baser passions of mankind.

Lord Wynchgate—for he it was who sat at the head of the table—rose with an oath, and flung his cards upon the table.

All turned and looked at him, with an oath. "Curse it, Dogwood," he exclaimed with another oath, to the man who sat beside him. "Take the money. I play no more tonight. My luck is out."

"Ha! ha!" laughed Lord Dogwood, with a third oath. "Your mind is not on the cards. Who is the latest young beauty, pray, who so absorbs you. I hear a whisper in town of a certain misadventure of yours—"

"Dogwood," said Wynchgate, clinching his fist, "have a care, man, or you shall measure the length of my sword."

Both noblemen faced each other, their hands upon their swords.

"My lords, my lords!" pleaded a distinguished-looking man of more advanced years, who sat at one side of the table and in whose features the habitués of diplomatic circles would have recognized the handsome lineaments of the Marquis of Frogwater, British Ambassador to Siam. "Let us have no quarrelling. Come, Wynchgate, come, Dogwood," he continued, with a mild oath, "put up your swords. It were a shame to waste time in private quarrelling. They may be needed all too soon in Cochin China, or, for the matter of that," he added sadly, "in Cambodia or in Dutch Guiana."

"Frogwater," said young Lord Dogwood, with a generous flush, "I was wrong. Wynchgate, your hand."

The two noblemen shook hands.

"My friends," said Lord Wynchgate, "in asking you to abandon our game, I had an end in view. I ask your help in an affair of the heart."

"Ha! excellent!" exclaimed the five noblemen. "We are with you heart and soul."

"I propose this night," continued Wynchgate, "with your help to carry off a young girl, a female!"

"An abduction!" exclaimed the Ambassador somewhat sternly. "Wynchgate, I cannot countenance this."

"Mistake me not," said the Earl, "I intend to abduce her. But I propose nothing dishonourable. It is my firm resolve to offer her marriage."

"Then," said Lord Frogwater, "I am with you."

"Gentlemen," concluded Wynchgate, "all is ready. A coach is below. I have provided masks, pistols, and black cloaks. Follow me."

A few moments later, a coach, with the blinds drawn, in which were six noblemen armed to the teeth, might have been seen, were it not for the darkness, approaching the humble lodging in which Winnifred Clair was sheltered.

But what it did when it got there we must leave to another chapter.

V

THE ABDUCTION

The hour was twenty minutes to ten on the evening described in our last chapter.

Winnifred Clair was seated, still fully dressed, at the window of the bedroom looking out over the great city.

A light tap came at the door.

"If it's a fried egg," called Winnifred softly, "I do not need it. I ate yesterday."

"No," said the voice of the landlady. "You are wanted below."

"I!" exclaimed Winifred, "below!"

"You," said the landlady, "below. A party of gentlemen have called for you."

"Gentlemen," exclaimed Winnifred, putting her hand to her brow in perplexity, "for me! at this late hour! Here! This evening! In this house?"

"Yes," repeated the landlady, "six gentlemen. They arrived in a closed coach. They are all closely masked and heavily armed. They beg you will descend at once."

"Just Heaven!" cried the Unhappy Girl. "Is it possible that they mean to abduce me?"

"They do," said the landlady. "They said so!"

"Alas!" cried Winnifred, "I am powerless. Tell them"—she hesitated—"tell them I will be down immediately. Let them not come up. Keep them below on any pretext. Show them an album. Let them look at the gold fish. Anything, but not here! I shall be ready in a moment."

Feverishly she made herself ready. As hastily as possible she removed all traces of tears from her face. She threw about her shoulders an opera cloak, and with a light Venetian scarf half concealed the beauty of her hair and features. "Abduced!" she murmured, "and by six of them! I think she said six. Oh! the horror of it!" A touch of powder to her cheeks and a slight blackening of her eyebrows, and the courageous girl was ready.

Lord Wynchgate and his companions—for they it was, that is to say, they were it—sat below in the sitting room looking at the albums. "Woman," said Lord Wynchgate to the landlady with an oath, "let her hurry up. We have seen enough of these. We can wait no longer."

"I am here," cried a clear voice upon the threshold, and Winnifred stood before them. "My lords, for I divine who you are and wherefore you have come, take me, do your worst with me, but spare, oh spare! this humble companion of my sorrow."

"Right-oh!" said Lord Dogwood, with a brutal laugh.

"Enough," exclaimed Wynchgate, and seizing Winnifred by the wrist he dragged her forth out of the house and out upon the street.

But something in the brutal violence of his behaviour seemed to kindle for the moment a spark of manly feeling, if such there were, in the breasts of his companions.

"Wynchgate," cried young Lord Dogwood, "my mind misgives me. I doubt if this is a gentlemanly thing to do. I'll have no further hand in it."

A chorus of approval from his companions endorsed his utterance. For a moment they hesitated.

"Nay," cried Winnifred, turning to confront the masked faces that stood about her. "Go forward with your fell design. I am here. I am helpless. Let no prayers stay your hand. Go to it."

"Have done with this!" cried Wynchgate with a brutal oath. "Shove her in the coach."

But at the very moment the sound of hurrying foot-steps was heard and a clear, ringing, manly, well-toned, vibrating voice cried, "Hold! Stop! Desist! Have a care, titled villain, or I will strike you to the earth."

A tall aristocratic form bounded out of the darkness.

"Gentlemen," cried Wynchgate, releasing his hold upon the frightened girl, "we are betrayed. Save yourselves. To the coach."

In another instant the six noblemen had leaped into the coach and disappeared down the street.

Winnifred, still half inanimate with fright, turned to her rescuer and saw before her the form and linea-ments of the Unknown Stranger who had thus twice stood between her and disaster. Half fainting, she fell swooning into his arms.

"Dear lady," he exclaimed, "rouse yourself. You are safe. Let me restore you to your home!"

"That voice!" cried Winnifred, resuming conscious-ness. "It is my benefactor."

She would have swooned again, but the Unknown lifted her bodily up the steps of her home and leant her against the door.

"Farewell," he said, in a voice resonant with gloom.

"Oh, sir!" cried the unhappy girl, "let one who owes so much to one who has saved her in her hour of need at least know his name."

But the stranger, with a mournful gesture of fare-well, had disappeared as rapidly as he had come.

But as to why he had disappeared, we must ask our reader's patience for another chapter.

### VI

#### THE UNKNOWN

The scene is now shifted, sideways and forwards, so as to put it at Muddlenut Chase, and to make it a fort-night later than the events related in the last chapter.

Winnifred is now at the Chase as the guest of the Mar-quis and Marchioness. There her bruised soul finds peace.

The Chase itself was one of those typical country homes which are, or were till yesterday, the glory of England. The approach to the Chase lay through twenty miles of glorious forest, filled with fallow deer and wild bulls. The house itself, dating from the time of the Plantagenets, was surrounded by a moat covered with broad lilies and floating green scum. Magnificent peacocks sunned them-selves on the terraces, while from the surrounding shrub-beries there rose the soft murmur of doves, pigeons, bats, owls and partridges.

Here sat Winnifred Clair day after day upon the ter-race recovering her strength, under the tender solicitude of the Marchioness.

Each day the girl urged upon her noble hostess the necessity of her departure. "Nay," said the Marchion-ess, with gentle insistence, "stay where you are. Your soul is bruised. You must rest."

"Alas!" cried Winnifred, "who am I that I should rest? Alone, despised, buffeted by fate, what right have I to your kindness?"

"Miss Clair," replied the noble lady, "wait till you are stronger. There is something that I wish to say to you."

Then at last one morning when Winnifred's temperature had fallen to ninety-eight point three, the Marchioness spoke.

"Miss Clair," she said, in a voice which throbbed with emotion,—"Winnifred, if I may so call you. Lord Muddlenut and I have formed a plan for your future. It is our dearest wish that you should marry our son."

"Alas!" cried Winnifred, while tears rose in her eyes, "it cannot be!"

"Say not so," cried the Marchioness. "Our son, Lord Mordaunt Muddlenut, is young, handsome, all that a girl could desire. After months of wandering he returns to us this morning. It is our dearest wish to see him married and established. We offer you his hand."

"Indeed," replied Winnifred, while her tears fell even more freely, "I seem to requite but ill the kindness that you show. Alas! my heart is no longer in my keeping."

"Where is it?" cried the Marchioness.

"It is another's. One whose very name I do not know, holds it in his keeping."

But at this moment a blithe, gladsome step was heard upon the flagstones of the terrace. A manly, ringing voice which sent a thrill to Winnifred's heart, cried "Mother!" and in another instant Lord Mordaunt Muddlenut, for he it was, had folded the Marchioness to his heart.

Winnifred rose, her heart beating wildly. One glance was enough. The newcomer, Lord Mordaunt, was none

other than the Unknown, the Unaccountable, to whose
protection she had twice owed her life.

With a wild cry Winnifred Clair leaped across the
flagstones of the terrace and fled into the park.

### VII

#### THE PROPOSAL

They stood beneath the great trees of the ancestral park,
into which Lord Mordaunt had followed Winnifred at a
single bound.  All about them was the radiance of early
June.

Lord Mordaunt knelt on one knee on the greensward,
and with a touch in which respect and reverence were
mingled with the deepest and manliest emotion, he took
between his finger and thumb the tip of the girl's gloved
hand.

"Miss Clair," he uttered, in a voice suffused with the
deepest yearning, yet vibrating with the most profound
respect, "Miss Clair—Winnifred—hear me, I implore!"

"Alas," cried Winnifred, struggling in vain to disen-
gage the tip of her glove from the impetuous clasp of
the young nobleman.  "Alas! whither can I fly!  I do not
know my way through the wood and there are bulls in
all directions.  I am not used to them!  Lord Mordaunt,
I implore you, let the tears of one but little skilled in the
art of dissimulation—"

"Nay, Winnifred," said the Young Earl, "fly not.  Hear
me out!"

"Let me fly," begged the unhappy girl.

"You must not fly," pleaded Mordaunt.  "Let me first,
here upon bended knee convey to you the expression of

a devotion, a love, as ardent and as deep as ever burned in a human heart. Winnifred! be my bride!"

"Oh, sir," sobbed Winnifred, "if the knowledge of a gratitude, a thankfulness from one whose heart will ever treasure as its proudest memory the recollection of one who did for one all that one could have wanted done for one, if this be some poor guerdon, let it suffice. But, alas, my birth, the dark secret of my birth forbids—"

"Nay," cried Mordaunt, leaping now to his feet, "your birth is all right. I have looked into it myself. It is as good—or nearly as good—as my own. Till I knew this, my lips were sealed by duty. While I supposed that you had a lower birth and I an upper, I was bound to silence. But come with me to the house. There is one arrived with me who will explain all."

Hand in hand the lovers, for such they now were, returned to the Chase. There in the great hall the Marquis and the Marchioness were standing ready to greet them.

"My child!" exclaimed the noble lady, as she folded Winnifred to her heart.

Then she turned to her son. "Let her know all!" she cried.

Lord Mordaunt stepped across the room to a curtain. He drew it aside, and there stepped forth Mr. Bonehead, the old lawyer who had cast Winnifred upon the world.

"Miss Clair," said the lawyer, advancing and taking the girl's hand for a moment in a kindly clasp, "the time has come for me to explain all. You are not, you never were, the penniless girl that you suppose. Under the terms of your father's will, I was called upon to act a part and to throw you upon the world. It was my client's wish, and I followed it. I told you, quite truthfully, that I had put part of your money into options in an oil well.

Miss Clair, that well is now producing a million gallons of gasoline a month!"

"A million gallons!" cried Winnifred.  "I can never use it."

"Wait till you own a motor car, Miss Winnifred," said the lawyer.

"Then I am rich!" exclaimed the bewildered girl.

"Rich beyond your dreams," answered the lawyer. "Miss Clair, you own in your own right about half of the State of Texas—I think it is Texas, at any rate either Texas or Rhode Island, or one of those big states in America.  More than this, I have invested your property since your father's death so wisely that even after paying the income tax and the property tax, the inheritance tax, the dog tax and the tax on amusements you will still have one half of one per cent. to spend."

Winnifred clasped her hands.

"I knew it all the time," said Lord Mordaunt, drawing the girl to his embrace.  "I found it out through this good man."

"We knew it too," said the Marchioness.  "Can you forgive us, darling, our little plot for your welfare.  Had we not done this Mordaunt might have had to follow you over to America and chase you all around Newport and Narragansett at a fearful expense."

"How can I thank you enough?" cried Winnifred. Then she added eagerly, "And my birth, my descent?"

"It is all right," interjected the Old Lawyer.  "It is A-1. Your father, who died before you were born, quite a little time before, belonged to the very highest peerage of Wales.  You are descended directly from Claer-ap-Claer, who murdered Owen Glendower.  Your mother we are still tracing up.  But we have already connected her with Floyd-ap-Floyd who murdered Prince Llewellyn."

"Oh, sir," cried the grateful girl. "I only hope I may prove worthy of them!"

"One thing more," said Lord Mordaunt, and stepping over to another curtain he drew it aside and there emerged Lord Wynchgate.

He stood before Winnifred, a manly contrition struggling upon features which, but for the evil courses of him who wore them, might have been almost presentable.

"Miss Clair," he said, "I ask your pardon. I tried to carry you off. I never will again. But before we part let me say that my acquaintance with you has made me a better man, broader, bigger and, I hope, deeper."

With a profound bow, Lord Wynchgate took his leave.


### VIII

#### WEDDED AT LAST

Lord Mordaunt and his bride were married forthwith in the parish church of Muddlenut Chase. With Winnifred's money they have drained the moat, rebuilt the Chase, and chased the bulls out of the park. They have six childern, so far, and are respected, honoured and revered in the countryside far and wide, over a radius of twenty miles in circumference.

# Abolishing the Heroine

*(A Plea that Fewer Heroines and More Crimes Would
Add Sprightliness to our Fiction)*

I WANT to lead a bold national movement for the aboli-
tion of the Heroine out of our literature. In my opinion the time has come when this young woman has grown
to be a nuisance. All our stories would be much better
without her. She just clutters them all up.

What I mean is this. Open any story of adventure or
excitement or crime; and you find that it runs along
admirably for a certain distance but just when it is getting exciting and worth while, in steps The Heroine and
spoils it.

Let me give an example of what I mean. Every reader
of up-to-date fiction will recognize the thing in a minute. Call the story:

## AFTER MIDNIGHT
### or,
*How the Heroine Spoils a Crime Story*

Now we begin.

John Curbstone is a young bachelor clubman of great
wealth. He is a man of culture, being a graduate of Harvard University. (*In all these stories Harvard is the best
place to graduate them from. It sounds far better than
the Minnesota Agricultural College.*) He is a keen sportsman because this enables him to wear the right kind of
breeches for the illustrator to use,—shaped like a ham

at the hips and tight at the knee. All Harvard graduates wear them. He plays polo, golf and bridge, drinks brandy and soda, and has one of those clean-shaven aristocratic faces seen only in a democratic country.

He lives,—with a butler who doesn't count and some servants who don't come into the story,—in a large sandstone house on Riverside Drive. This family residence had belonged to Curbstone's father before him, which shows that his family is an old one. Indeed the Curbstones have lived on that street for thirty years which gives young Curbstone a sense of *noblesse oblige* towards the whole district up to 125th Street.

The scene is now laid.

Returning home late one night from his club (he never leaves his club till it shuts), John realizes that his house has been burglarized. In the dining-room the side-board has been rudely broken open, apparently with a jimmy. A glass still reeking with ginger ale rests on the top of it; an open bottle, evidently opened with a jimmy, is near it. In the corner of the room the iron safe has been forced, most likely with a jimmy. There is a litter of bonds and family jewelry on the floor. It is clear that the burglar has been interrupted at his work. It is likely that he is still on the premises.

John Curbstone stands motionless in the centre of the room listening. There is absolute silence. There is no sound in the still house but the ticking of a clock.

Then as Curbstone listens intently his ear just catches a faint sound from behind the closed door of a cupboard. The burglar must be there hidden behind the door! Curbstone draws his revolver from his hip (it was the revolver that he had used that night for playing poker), and levels it full at the cupboard.

"I shall count three," he announced in clear even tones,

"and if you are not out of that cupboard then, I shall fire through the door." Curbstone counted, still in clear, even tones, "One, two,"—but just as he was going to say three, an agitated voice exclaimed, "Oh, please don't shoot," the cupboard door opened and there stepped out into the room,—

A girl! Just think of it, a girl! And what makes it worse, only a mere slip of a girl! If it had been a big one,—you know, one of those great big fine-looking ones it wouldn't have been so bad. But this one is only a slip!

She came forward towards John Curbstone, her large blue eyes distracted with apprehension. She was in evening dress with a light peignoir, or baignoire or boudoir, thrown about her shoulders. "Please don't shoot," she repeated (at this point in the story the illustrator gets in his work and doesn't have to read any further).

Curbstone lowered his revolver.

"So," he said, sternly, "you are a *thief*." The girl shuddered into herself. The word seemed to sting her. She didn't mind breaking open Curbstone's safe but when she was called a "thief" she was stung.

"I'm not a thief," she panted.

There! Let us leave her there a little panting while I talk about her. I have seen that girl come out of that cupboard and similar places so often that I'm sick of her. I know that just as soon as the man in the story opens a cupboard door, or draws aside a curtain, out comes "a slip of a girl." He hears a noise in the attic. What is there? A girl. He hears some one in the cellar. Who is it? A girl. Who did it? A girl, a mere child!

Now what I say is that this kind of thing is ruining our best stories. They start in excitement and end in slush. In the story I have just outlined when the cupboard door opened, Curbstone ought to have been confronted with something worth while—a burglar—a real one, with short-cropped hair under a low cap, with a dark lantern in one hand and a jimmy in the other. Then when Curbstone said sternly, "So, you are a thief," the burglar could answer, "I sure am." Or better still the door might open, and three burglars come out, or even four, in short a cupboardful of burglars. Even if it has to be a girl, why make her a "slip"? Why not let it read, "There stepped out of the cupboard a great big girl about six feet high and at least seventeen inches around the neck." In any such case the adventure and excitement of the story could continue. There could be a tremendous fight,—in which let us hope, they might have killed Curbstone and sent him back to his club dead and so put him out of literature for ever.

But it is understood that a man, or at least a Harvard graduate, must not use force against a slip of a girl. So in default of a decent ending the story has to run off into slush.

Ending it up is quite simple: it would probably be done somewhat as follows:

"I'm not a thief," she repeated.

She looked at him for a minute proudly defiant: for she came of an old family just as proud as his. Her people had had the same summer cottage in the Adirondacks for six years running.

John Curbstone looked at the girl calmly. "Miss Chetwynde," he said, "if you are not a thief, will you kindly tell me why you tried to rob my safe?" When he calls her "Miss Chetwynde," this is meant as an indication to the reader that Curbstone knows her.

"Oh, how can I explain?" exclaimed the girl wringing her hands, "you wouldn't understand! you couldn't understand! I wanted the money so much! There is so much to do with money, so much suffering to alleviate! And you with your great wealth you do nothing! Ask yourself," she continued, her voice thrilled with earnestness, "what do you do for social service, for sanitation, for reforestation, for the girl guides, for the boy scouts—"

John Curbstone hung his head with a groan. "Nothing," he said.

"This afternoon," the girl went on, "I came to your office. I asked you for a hundred thousand dollars for the Metropolitan Police Picnic, and you refused!"

"Miss Chetwynde," said Curbstone in the same clear even tones that he had used earlier, "I did *not* refuse. I asked you to marry me. It was you who did me the honour of refusal."

"It maddened me," the girl went on, "and I determined to take your money, yes, *take* it, and give it to the Police. If that is stealing I don't care. Then I came here to rob you. The Police themselves lent me the jimmy! Oh, it was madness, madness,—"

She paused. They were both silent for a moment. Then Curbstone reached out and took her by the hand.

"Miss Chetwynde—Alice," he said, "don't you think that we have both been a little wrong—"

She looked up timidly. "A little, John dear," she murmured.

.    .    .    .    .    .    .

And with that the story is ended, and looks just like any of the other two hundred that are published every month. But what I want is to see that disturbing girl cut out, and real adventure put in,—in short more crime and plenty of it.

# The Reading Public. A Book Store Study

"Wish to look about the store? Oh, oh, by all means, sir," he said.

Then as he rubbed his hands together in an urbane fashion he directed a piercing glance at me through his spectacles.

"You'll find some things that might interest you," he said, "in the back of the store on the left. We have there a series of reprints—*Universal Knowledge from Aristotle to Arthur Balfour*—at seventeen cents. Or perhaps you might like to look over the *Pantheon of Dead Authors* at ten cents. Mr. Sparrow," he called, "just show this gentleman our classical reprints—the ten-cent series."

With that he waved his hand to an assistant and dismissed me from his thought.

In other words, he had divined me in a moment. There was no use in my having bought a sage-green fedora in Broadway, and a sporting tie done up crosswise with spots as big as nickels. These little adornments can never hide the soul within. I was a professor, and he knew it, or at least, as part of his business, he could divine it on the instant.

The sales manager of the biggest book store for ten blocks cannot be deceived in a customer. And he knew, of course, that, as a professor, I was no good. I had come to the store, as all professors go to book stores, just as a wasp comes to an open jar of marmalade. He knew that I would hang around for two hours, get in everybody's

220

way, and finally buy a cheap reprint of the *Dialogues of Plato,* or the *Prose Works of John Milton,* or *Locke on the Human Understanding,* or some trash of that sort.

As for real taste in literature—the ability to appreciate at its worth a dollar-fifty novel of last month, in a spring jacket with a tango frontispiece—I hadn't got it and he knew it.

He despised me, of course. But it is a maxim of the book business that a professor standing up in a corner buried in a book looks well in a store. The real customers like it.

So it was that even so up-to-date a manager as Mr. Sellyer tolerated my presence in a back corner of his store: and so it was that I had an opportunity of noting something of his methods with his real customers—methods so successful, I may say, that he is rightly looked upon by all the publishing business as one of the mainstays of literature in America.

I had no intention of standing in the place and listening as a spy. In fact, to tell the truth, I had become immediately interested in a new translation of the *Moral Discourses of Epictetus.* The book was very neatly printed, quite well bound and was offered at eighteen cents; so that for the moment I was strongly tempted to buy it, though it seemed best to take a dip into it first.

I had hardly read more than the first three chapters when my attention was diverted by a conversation going on in the front of the store.

"You're quite sure it's his *latest?*" a fashionably dressed lady was saying to Mr. Sellyer.

"Oh, yes, Mrs. Rasselyer," answered the manager. "I assure you this is his very latest. In fact, they only came in yesterday."

As he spoke, he indicated with his hand a huge pile of

books, gayly jacketed in white and blue. I could make out the title in big gilt lettering—*GOLDEN DREAMS*.

"Oh, yes," repeated Mr. Sellyer. "This is Mr. Slush's latest book. It's having a wonderful sale."

"That's all right, then," said the lady. "You see, one sometimes gets taken in so: I came in here last week and took two that seemed very nice, and I never noticed till I got home that they were both old books, published, I think, six months ago."

"Oh, dear me, Mrs. Rasselyer," said the manager in an apologetic tone, "I'm extremely sorry. Pray let us send for them and exchange them for you."

"Oh, it does not matter," said the lady; "of course I didn't read them. I gave them to my maid. She probably wouldn't know the difference, anyway."

"I suppose not," said Mr. Sellyer, with a condescending smile. "But of course, madam," he went on, falling into the easy chat of the fashionable bookman, "such mistakes are bound to happen sometimes. We had a very painful case only yesterday. One of our oldest customers came in in a great hurry to buy books to take on the steamer, and before we realised what he had done—selecting the books I suppose merely by the titles, as some gentlemen are apt to do—he had taken two of last year's books. We wired at once to the steamer, but I'm afraid it's too late."

"But now, this book," said the lady, idly turning over the leaves, "is it good? What is it about?"

"It's an extremely *powerful* thing," said Mr. Sellyer, "in fact, *masterly*. The critics are saying that it's perhaps *the* most powerful book of the season. It has a—" And here Mr. Sellyer paused, and somehow his manner reminded me of my own when I am explaining to a university class something that I don't know myself—"It has a—a—*power*, so to speak—a very exceptional power; in fact, one may say without exaggeration it is the most *powerful* book of the month. Indeed," he added, getting on to easier ground, "it's having a perfectly wonderful sale."

"You seem to have a great many of them," said the lady.

"Oh, we have to," answered the manager. "There's a regular rush on the book. Indeed, you know it's a book that is bound to make a sensation. In fact, in certain quarters, they are saying that it's a book that ought not to—" And here Mr. Sellyer's voice became so low and ingratiating that I couldn't hear the rest of the sentence.

"Oh, really!" said Mrs. Rasselyer. "Well, I think I'll take it then. One ought to see what these talked-of things are about, anyway."

She had already begun to button her gloves, and to read-just her feather boa with which she had been knocking the Easter cards off the counter. Then she suddenly remembered something.

"Oh, I was forgetting," she said. "Will you send something to the house for Mr. Rasselyer at the same time? He's going down to Virginia for the vacation. You know the kind of thing he likes, do you not?"

"Oh, perfectly, madam," said the manager. "Mr. Rasselyer generally reads works of—er—I think he buys mostly books on—er—"

"Oh, travel and that sort of thing," said the lady.

"Precisely. I think we have here," and he pointed to the counter on the left, "what Mr. Rasselyer wants."

He indicated a row of handsome books—*"Seven Weeks in the Sahara,* seven dollars; *Six Months in a Waggon,* six-fifty net; *Afternoons in an Oxcart,* two volumes, four-thirty, with twenty off."

"I think he has read those," said Mrs. Rasselyer. "At least there are a good many at home that seem like that."

"Oh, very possibly—but here, now, *Among the Canni-*

*bals of Corfu*—yes, that I think he has had—*Among the*
—that, too, I think—but this I am certain he would like,
just in this morning—*Among the Monkeys of New Guinea*
—ten dollars, net."

And with this Mr. Sellyer laid his hand on a pile of new
books, apparently as numerous as the huge pile of *Golden
Dreams*.

"*Among the Monkeys*," he repeated, almost caressingly.

"It seems rather expensive," said the lady.

"Oh, very much so—a most expensive book," the manager repeated in a tone of enthusiasm.  "You see, Mrs.
Rasselyer, it's the illustrations, actual photographs"—he ran
the leaves over in his fingers—"of actual monkeys, taken
with the camera—and the paper, you notice—in fact,
madam, the book costs, the mere manufacture of it, nine
dollars and ninety cents—of course we make no profit on
it.  But it's a book we like to handle."

Everybody likes to be taken into the details of technical
business; and of course everybody likes to know that a
bookseller is losing money.  These, I realised, were two
axioms in the methods of Mr. Sellyer.

So very naturally Mrs. Rasselyer bought *Among the
Monkeys,* and in another moment Mr. Sellyer was direct-
ing a clerk to write down an address on Fifth Avenue, and
was bowing deeply as he showed the lady out of the door.

As he turned back to his counter his manner seemed
much changed.

"That Monkey book," I heard him murmur to his assistant, "is going to be a pretty stiff proposition."

But he had no time for further speculation.

Another lady entered.

This time even to an eye less trained than Mr. Sellyer's,
the deep, expensive mourning and the pensive face proclaimed the sentimental widow.

"Something new in fiction," repeated the manager, "yes, madam—here's a charming thing—*Golden Dreams*"—he hung lovingly on the words—"a very sweet story, singularly sweet; in fact, madam, the critics are saying it is the sweetest thing that Mr. Slush has done."

"Is it good?" said the lady.   I began to realise that all customers asked this.

"A charming book," said the manager.   "It's a love story —very simple and sweet, yet wonderfully charming.   Indeed, the reviews say it's the most charming book of the month.   My wife was reading it aloud only last night.   She could hardly read for tears."

"I suppose it's quite a safe book, is it?" asked the widow. "I want it for my little daughter."

"Oh, quite safe," said Mr. Sellyer, with an almost parental tone, "in fact, written quite in the old style, like the dear old books of the past—quite like"—here Mr. Sellyer paused with a certain slight haze of doubt visible in his eye—"like Dickens and Fielding and Sterne and so on. We sell a great many to the clergy, madam."

The lady bought *Golden Dreams,* received it wrapped up in green enamelled paper, and passed out.

"Have you any good light reading for vacation time?" called out the next customer in a loud, breezy voice—he had the air of a stock broker starting on a holiday.

"Yes," said Mr. Sellyer, and his face almost broke into a laugh as he answered, "here's an excellent thing—*Golden Dreams*—quite the most humorous book of the season— simply screaming—my wife was reading it aloud only yesterday.   She could hardly read for laughing."

"What's the price, one dollar?   One-fifty.   All right, wrap it up."   There was a clink of money on the counter, and the customer was gone.   I began to see exactly where professors and college people who want copies of

*Epictetus* at 18 cents and sections of *World Reprints of Literature* at 12 cents a section come in, in the book trade.

"Yes, Judge!" said the manager to the next customer, a huge, dignified personage in a wide-awake hat, "sea stories? Certainly. Excellent reading, no doubt, when the brain is overcharged as yours must be. Here is the very latest—*Among the Monkeys of New Guinea*, ten dollars, reduced to four-fifty. The manufacture alone costs six-eighty. We're selling it out. Thank you, Judge. Send it? Yes. Good morning."

After that the customers came and went in a string. I noticed that though the store was filled with books—ten thousand of them, at a guess—Mr. Sellyer was apparently only selling two. Every woman who entered went away with *Golden Dreams:* every man was given a copy of the *Monkeys of New Guinea*. To one lady *Golden Dreams* was sold as exactly the reading for a holiday, to another as the very book to read *after* a holiday; another bought it as a book for a rainy day, and a fourth as the right sort of reading for a fine day. The Monkeys was sold as a sea story, a land story, a story of the jungle, and a story of the mountains, and it was put at a price corresponding to Mr. Sellyer's estimate of the purchaser.

At last after a busy two hours, the store grew empty for a moment.

"Wilfred," said Mr. Sellyer, turning to his chief assistant, "I am going out to lunch. Keep those two books running as hard as you can. We'll try them for another day and then cut them right out. And I'll drop round to Dockem & Discount, the publishers, and make a kick about them, and see what they'll do."

I felt that I had lingered long enough. I drew near with the *Epictetus* in my hand.

"Yes, sir," said Mr. Sellyer, professional again in a moment. "*Epictetus?* A charming thing. Eighteen cents. Thank you. Perhaps we have some other things there that might interest you. We have a few second-hand things in the alcove there that you might care to look at. There's an *Aristotle,* two volumes—a very fine thing— practically illegible, that you might like: and a *Cicero* came in yesterday—very choice—damaged by damp—and I think we have a *Machiavelli,* quite exceptional—practically torn to pieces, and the covers gone—a very rare old thing, sir, if you're an expert."

"No, thanks," I said. And then from a curiosity that had been growing in me and that I couldn't resist, "That book—*Golden Dreams,*" I said, "you seem to think it a very wonderful work?"

Mr. Sellyer directed one of his shrewd glances at me. He knew I didn't want to buy the book, and perhaps, like lesser people, he had his off moments of confidence.

He shook his head.

"A bad business," he said. "The publishers have unloaded the thing on us, and we have to do what we can. They're stuck with it, I understand, and they look to us to help them. They're advertising it largely and may pull it off. Of course, there's just a chance. One can't tell. It's just possible we may get the church people down on it and if so we're all right. But short of that we'll never make it. I imagine it's perfectly rotten."

"Haven't you read it?" I asked.

"Dear me, no!" said the manager. His air was that of a milkman who is offered a glass of his own milk. "A pretty time I'd have if I tried to *read* the new books. It's quite enough to keep track of them without that."

"But those people," I went on, deeply perplexed, "who bought the book. Won't they be disappointed?"

Mr. Sellyer shook his head. "Oh, no," he said; "you see, they won't *read* it. They never do."

"But at any rate," I insisted, "your wife thought it a fine story."

Mr. Sellyer smiled widely.

"I am not married, sir," he said.

# How to Lose Money (for Amateurs)

WE may define business in a broad, general way as the art of losing money.

This is only a rough-and-ready definition to which numerous exceptions will be found.

Indeed, very often, business, even if losing a certain amount of money, is carried on for other reasons. As one of my big-business friends said to me the other day, "What else can I do?" Many of my business friends—the big ones—ask me that: what else can they do? I don't know what else they can do.

Or very often a business connection is of such long standing, of generations, perhaps, that it is difficult to stop. I am thinking here of my friend Sir John Overwarp, the big thread man. Sir John is the senior partner of Overwarp, Underwarp and Shuttle. In fact he *is* Overwarp, Underwarp and Shuttle. They are probably the biggest thread people in the world. They are *the* thread people. They have works in Sheffield, Bradfield, Oldfield—in short, they have so many works they don't know where they are.

Well, the other day Sir John said to me (he speaks to me): "We've been in thread now for five generations. I don't know how I could get out of it." After five generations in thread you get all tangled up in it. Somebody told me that Sir John's shareholders are going to let him out. It'll be nice of them if they do.

But business habit is business habit. I knew a man, one of the McDuffs of Duff (they came from Duff) who had been in Scotch whiskey, and in nothing else, for years and years. He had travelled round the world in it four times. It seemed to follow him. You could notice it.

Then there's the sense of responsibility—I mean, responsibility to other people. I know quite well the French financier, the Baron de Citrouille (it is pronounced *Citrouille*) who brought a great quantity of French money out to America, and lost it here. He couldn't have lost the half of it in France, but here he was able to do what is called "spread his loss." Some of the big men can spread their loss over half the continent.

But these of course are the *big* men—what are called the Captains of Industry. It is not wise to try to begin with discussing such large-scale operations as theirs. It might give the beginner a sense of despair. Some of these men are known to lose a million dollars a day. The business beginner asks, "Can I do that?" I answer, "Not yet, but you can learn."

One has to realize that these are selected men, winnowed out, as it were, from the crowd; they are men who probably had even at the beginning a flair for business and kept on getting more and more flair. The word flair is French. It is pronounced flair and means in a general way more or less what we call in English a flair.

These big men, indeed, are distinguished not so much by what they do as by what they can't do or won't do. I once knew (I knew him only once) Sir Humphrey Dumphrey, the big electrical man: he was probably the biggest electrical man in Europe, except perhaps the Italians, Nitti and Dotti. Sir Humphrey said to me: "Look at me. I can't do fractions." I looked at him. He couldn't do them.

Or take Sir Hamstein Gorfinkel, the great British financier. He said he couldn't recite the Lord's Prayer: couldn't or wouldn't.

But these men are in a class by themselves.

When I say I want to talk about business and how money can be lost, even in a small way, I naturally wish to begin with simple things.   Young people just entering on life realize that if only they had money now, even a moderate sum, they could find opportunities to lose it that would never come later.

There are so many choices to be made, such a difficulty in selecting a career, that young people need help.   "Should I live in the country?" a young lady asked me at a reception.   "Yes," I said, "away in, as far as you can get."

"My son," wrote an old friend, "shows every disposition to be a stock-broker.   What should I do about it?" "Shoot him," I answered.

One should start with some of the simpler ways of losing money, such as chicken raising, dry duck farming, keeping bees and wasps, along with such things as horticulture and germicide.   Bigger things could come later, such as how to build a transcontinental navy.   One must start humbly.

# My Fishing Pond

*(I told this story so often and so successfully as a story that at last I went and told it to the Editor of the* Atlantic Monthly, *and he told it to all the world. But there is no harm in retelling it here.)*

It lies embowered in a little cup of the hills, my fishing pond. I made a last trip to it, just as the season ended, when the autumn leaves of its great trees were turning colour and rustling down to rest upon the still black water. So steep are the banks, so old and high the trees, that scarcely a puff of wind ever ruffles the surface of the pond. All around it, it is as if the world was stilled into silence, and time blended into eternity.

I realized again as I looked at the pond what a beautiful, secluded spot it was, how natural its appeal to the heart of the angler. You turn off a country road, go sideways across a meadow and over a hill and there it lies—a sheet of still water, with high, high banks, grown with great trees. Long years ago someone built a sawmill, all gone now, at the foot of the valley and threw back the water to make a pond, perhaps a quarter of a mile long. At the widest it must be nearly two hundred feet—the most skilful fisherman may make a full cast both ways. At the top end, where it runs narrow among stumps and rushes, there is no room to cast except with direction and great skill.

Let me say at once, so as to keep no mystery about it, that there are no fish in my pond. So far as I know there never have been. But I have never found that to make any difference. Certainly none to the men I bring here—

my chance visitors from the outside world—for an after-noon of casting.  If there are no fish in the pond, at least they never know it.  They never doubt it; they never ask; and I let it go at that.

It is well known hereabouts that I do not take anybody and everybody out to my fish pond.  I only care to invite people who can really fish, who can cast a line—experts, and especially people from a distance to whom the whole neighbourhood is new and attractive, the pond seen for the first time.  If I took out ordinary men, especially men near home, they would very likely notice that they got no fish.  The expert doesn't.  He knows trout fishing too well.  He knows that, even in a really fine pond, such as he sees mine is, there are days when not a trout will rise. He'll explain it to you himself, and, having explained it, he is all the better pleased if he turns out to be right and they don't rise.  Trout, as everyone knows who is an angler, never rise after a rain, nor before one; it is im-possible to get them to rise in the heat, and any chill in the air keeps them down.  The absolutely right day is a still, cloudy day, but even then there are certain kinds of clouds that prevent a rising of the trout.  Indeed I have only to say to one of my expert friends, "Queer, they didn't bite!" and he's off to a good start with an explana-tion.  There is such a tremendous lot to know about trout fishing that men who are keen on it can discuss theories of fishing by the hour.

Such theories we generally talk over—my guest of the occasion and I—as we make our preparations at the pond. You see I keep there all the apparatus that goes with fish-ing—a punt, with lockers in the sides of it—a neat little dock built out of cedar (Cedar attracts the trout.) and best of all a little shelter house, a quaint little place like a pagoda, close beside the water and yet under the trees.

Inside is tackle, all sorts of tackle, hanging round the walls in a mixture of carelessness and order.

"Look, old man," I say, "if you like to try a running pater noster, take this one." Or, "Have you ever seen these Japanese leads? No, they're not a gut, they're a sort of floss."

"I doubt if I can land one with that," he says.

"Perhaps not," I answer. In fact I'm sure he couldn't; there isn't any to land.

On pegs in the pagoda hangs a waterproof mackintosh or two—for you never know—you may be caught in a shower just when the trout are starting to rise. With that of course a sort of cellarette cupboard with decanters and bottles and ginger snaps and perhaps an odd pot of anchovy paste—no one wants to quit fishing for mere hunger. Nor does any real angler care to begin fishing without taking just a drop ("Just a touch; be careful; wo! wo!") of something to keep out the cold, or to wish good luck for the chances of the day.

I always find, when I bring out one of my friends, that these mere preparatives or preparations, these preliminaries of angling, are the best part of it. Often they take half an hour. There is so much to discuss—the question of weights of tackle, the colour of the fly to use and broad general questions of theory such as whether it matters what kind of a hat a man wears. It seems that trout will rise for some hats and for others not. One of my best guests, who has written a whole book on fly fishing, is particularly strong on hats and colour.

"I don't think I'd wear that hat, old man," he says, "much too dark for a day like this."

"I wore it all last month," I said.

"So you might, old man, but that was August. I

wouldn't wear a dark one in September, and that tie is too dark a blue, old man."

So I knew that that made it all right.  I kept the hat on. We had a grand afternoon; we got no fish.

I admit that the lack of fish in my pond requires sometimes a little tact in management.  The guest gets a little restless.  So I say to him, "You certainly have the knack of casting!" and he gets so absorbed in casting further and further that he forgets the fish.  Or I take him towards the upper end and he gets his line caught on bulrushes— that might be a bite.  Or if he still keeps restless, I say suddenly: "Hush!  Was that a fish jumped?"  That will silence any true angler instantly.  "You stand in the bow," I whisper, "and I'll gently paddle in that direction." It's the *whispering* that does it.  We are still a hundred yards away from any trout that could hear us, even if a trout was there.  But that makes no difference.  Some of the men I take out begin to whisper a mile away from the pond and come home whispering.

You see, after all, what with frogs jumping, and catching the line in bulrushes, or pulling up a water-logged chip nearly to the top, they don't really know—my guests don't—whether they have hooked something or not.  Indeed after a little lapse of time they think they did; they talk of the "big one I lost"—a thing over which any angler gets sentimental in retrospect.  "Do you remember," they say to me months later at our club in the city, "that big trout I lost up on your fish pond last summer!"

"Indeed I do," I say.

"Did you ever get him later on?"

"No, never," I answer.  In fact I'm darned sure I didn't; neither him nor any other.

Yet the illusion holds good.  And besides you never can tell.  There *might* be trout in the pond.  Why not?  After all, why shouldn't there be a trout in the pond? You take a pond like that and there ought to be trout in it!

Whenever the sight of the pond bursts on the eyes of a new guest he stands entranced. "What a wonderful place for trout!" he exclaims.

"Isn't it?" I answer.

"No wonder you'd get trout in a pond like that."

"No wonder at all."

"You don't need to stock it at all, I suppose?"

"Stock it!" I laugh at the idea! Stock a pond like that! Well, I guess not.

Perhaps one of the best and most alluring touches is fishing out of season—just a day or two after the season has closed. Any fisherman knows how keen is the regret at each expiring term—swallowed up and lost in the glory of the fading autumn. So if a guest turns up just then I say, "I know it's out of season, but I thought you might care to take a run out to the pond anyway and have a look at it." He can't resist. By the time he's in the pagoda and has a couple of small drinks ("Careful, not too much; wo! wo!") he decides there can be no harm in making a cast or two.

"I suppose," he says, "you never have any trouble with the inspectors?"

"Oh, no!" I answer, "they never think of troubling me." And with that we settle down to an afternoon of it.

"I'm glad," says the guest at the end, "that they weren't rising. After all we had just the same fun as if they were."

.    .    .    .    .    .    .

That's it—illusion! How much of life is like that. It's the *idea* of the thing that counts, not the reality. You don't need fish for fishing, any more than you need partridge for partridge shooting, or gold for gold mining . . . just the illusion or expectation.

So I am going back now to the city and to my club, where we shall fish all winter, hooking up the big ones, but losing the ones bigger still, hooking two trout at one throw—three at a throw!—and for me behind it all the memory of my fishing pond darkening under the falling leaves. . . . At least it has made my friends happy.

## MY LADDERS

### A Sequel to My Fishing Pond

Indulgent readers of the *Atlantic Monthly* will recall the fact that in that esteemed periodical a year ago, I wrote an account of My Fishing Pond. I described the beautiful little secluded spot in a woodland hollow in which it lay. I caught, I think, in words something of the autumn glory that fell on it with the falling leaves. I admitted, quite frankly, that as far as I knew there were no fish in it. But that, I explained, I kept to myself; it made no difference to the expert fishermen, my friends who came on a casual visit to cast a fly at my trout. They were all impressed with the wonderful surroundings, had never seen a trout pond of greater promise, and easily explained, over a friendly drink in my pagoda, the failure of a single day.

I realize now that I never should have published this in the *Atlantic*. The Editor and I must have offended some tributary god of fishing. Nemesis fell upon me. When the winter broke and the ice went, a great flood of water carried away the dam, and flung it, cement, logs and all, in a wild confusion of debris down the stream. There it lies now, and above it the pond, drained out flat to a bottom of wet weeds and old logs and stranded puddles—a feeble stream trickling through.

And the trout? Gone! washed clean away down the stream! I take my friends out now to the place and they explain it all to me until I can see it like a vision—the beautiful trout hurled away in spring flood and foam! My friends estimate them as anything from 2 miles of trout to 5 miles. But do you think those fishermen have lost interest? Not a bit! They are more keen on coming out to look at my pond and give advice about it than they were even in the days when we used, as they recall it, to haul out trout by the puntful.

They explain to me what to do. The miller who ran a little feed mill off the pond is going to rebuild the dam, and my friends tell me to put in "ladders" and the trout will all come back! A trout, it seems, will climb a ladder! I can hardly believe it, but they all tell me that; in fact I have learned to say nothing, just to look utterly disconsolate till the visiting expert says, "Have you thought of ladders?" And then I act the part of a man rescued from despair. They say it will take about three ladders of five feet each. How trout climb a ladder I don't know; it must be difficult for them to get hold of the rungs. But a man said in Scotland he has seen a trout climb 20 feet. It appears that if you go out in the autumn you can lie on the bank of the dam and watch the trout, splashing and climbing in the foam. Quite a lot of my friends are coming up here next autumn just to see them climb. And even if it is out of season, they may throw a hook at them!

Fishermen, in other words, are just unbeatable. Cut them off from fish, and they are just as happy over "ladders." So we sit now in my little pagoda, and someone says: "Talking about ladders, I must tell you—whoa! whoa! not too big a one." . . . And away we go, floating off on the Ladders of Imagination.

# While You're At It

*Expert Advice on Knocking Your House into Shape*

THIS house improvement stuff certainly appeals to me. You know what I mean—having your house all fixed up with new plumbing and heat and painting and everything. As soon as the government started the idea of improvement loans, it opened people's eyes. Lots of people, like myself, had gone on living in a house without realizing that there was anything wrong with it; and then there suddenly came to us all this idea of making a new home of it—that's the word, a *home*.

I got the first incentive to it one day when I noticed the pipes in the furnace room. They looked worn out. So I sent for a plumber and showed him the pipes, and he said right away, "These pipes are *gone*—clean *gone*." I hadn't realized that. I thought they were still there. "Look," he said, and took a hammer and started a big hole in one of them. "See that," he said. "That pipe's all corroded, it's oxidized—see! So's the other!"

He knocked the other to pieces.

"Can't you put in new ones?" I asked.

"Yes," he said, "I *could*, but if it was *me*, I wouldn't. You see, that furnace is too old; it's gone." He took his hammer and smashed in one side of the furnace. "See it break! You look at the metal, it's *acidulated!*"

"Well," I said, "you could fix it, couldn't you?"

"Yes," the plumber answered, "I *could*, but if it was me, I'd throw that furnace right out and put in the new self-acting thermostatic heat; it's fireless and without fuel

239

and cuts your cost per thermal unit by over a hundred per cent."

"Would you allow me anything on the old furnace?"

"I wouldn't bother with it if I were you; just throw it out. Of course it means changing the water pipes to your kitchen range. Do you know if they run through the range or are they geocentric?"

"I don't know," I said.

"Well, anyhow if it was me I'd throw all the pipes away and reset new ones."

.    .    .    .    .    .    .

So I got a kitchen range man to come and have a look. And he said right away that, while I was at it, I'd better throw the range out—just not bother with it. He explained that the whole range was *fused*—just think of it, *fused*—and probably had been for years, and I'd never known it.

So I said: "All right; throw it out and put in the new hypogastric kind that you say doesn't use heat at all but cooks with rheostats. It certainly seems wonderful."

So I put the range out and, on the man's advice, I didn't ask for any allowance on it. He told me it just wasn't worth bothering with.

But he said that I'd have to have the wall moved a couple of feet sideways. He said any building firm could do that in a day.

I sent for a builder and he came over with his foreman and they looked at the wall and said it was perfectly easy to move it—just a little brick and mortar and a few feet of scantling—no job at all and wouldn't cost much. At the same time they advised me not to do it; they wouldn't do it if it was them, neither of them, if it was either of them.

What they suggested—and they both thought of it—was not to shift the party wall itself only, but to carry it right up through the house; sink it below the basement and lift it right up through the roof. They reached up their hands above their heads to show how. Doing it that way, they said, I could put in the new hollow brick, the Delphic brick, that is practically air-proof.

I told them to go ahead, but they said that they'd need a contractor, because of the building permit, but that it was a simple matter to arrange.

They came back presently with the contractor. He took a look round and shook his head. He said he *could* carry the wall up. But much better knock down the house. The house, he showed me, was badly *hipped*. He said it must have *fluted*; probably had started with a small flute that had gone on fluting. He showed me a place in the dining-room where, just with a little builder's axe that he carried, he knocked out bucketfuls of plaster. It seems there was a *cyst* in the wall.

He strongly advised knocking the house down.

I asked about allowing anything for the material, but he said there was nothing in it either way. He said if you start picking over your brick (my brick) and trying to get the studding and joints out—well, you have your labour—I mean, his labour—or my labour, I didn't quite catch on *whose* labour, but anyway *your* labour, and *your* time, and what had you got? Nothing. He said if it was him he wouldn't bother with it.

.     .     .     .     .     .     .

They are knocking my house down now. I go and have a look at it every day, all disappearing in a cloud of white dust with bricks and plaster and rubbish going down a chute. I saw the books in my library going down yesterday. The contractor said there was no sense in picking them over; there'd be the labour and the time. He said if it was him, he'd read new ones.

So the house is disappearing. Just in time apparently! The further down they get with it, the more they realize the awful condition it was in! Just think of it! the roof had *hogged*—either had already hogged or was just going to hog any time! There was a five inch *sag* in the upper floor. He said it was on account of the *thrust*. Where the roof had *hogged*, a joint had *thrust*; that's what had made the *sag*, and it was the *sag* that had caused the *cyst* in the basement.

However, he'll get it down all right. He's a nice fellow and knows his job. He was telling me that he has knocked down a hundred houses already this year, and is knocking down a big hotel right now, and a church. He sent in a tender to go and knock down Westminster Abbey for the Coronation, but he was late.

.    .    .    .    .    .    .

Meantime I'm living in a room in a hotel. That will give me time, they say, to "turn round." I never felt till now that I needed time to turn round. But the builder and the contractor and everybody said I'd better take time to turn round.

.    .    .    .    .    .    .

Anyway that's all the time the hotel could give me. They didn't want me. They said that they would rather throw me into the river and get a new guest. But they'll keep me till I turn round.

After that they want the room. It seems there's a big hotel men's convention, and they want the whole hotel for the hotel men. That's only fair when you think of it.

# The Wizard of Finance

Down in the City itself, just below the residential street where the Mausoleum Club is situated, there stands overlooking Central Square the Grand Palaver Hotel. It is, in truth, at no great distance from the club, not half a minute in one's motor. In fact, one could almost walk it.

But in Central Square the quiet of Plutoria Avenue is exchanged for another atmosphere. There are fountains that splash unendingly and mingle their music with the sound of the motor-horns and the clatter of the cabs. There are real trees and little green benches, with people reading yesterday's newspaper, and grass cut into plots among the asphalt. There is at one end a statue of the first governor of the state, life-size, cut in stone; and at the other a statue of the last, ever so much larger than life, cast in bronze. And all the people who pass by pause and look at this statue and point at it with walking sticks, because it is of extraordinary interest; in fact, it is an example of the new electro-chemical process of casting by which you can cast a state governor any size you like, no matter what you start from. Those who know about such things explain what an interesting contrast the two statues are; for in the case of the governor of a hundred years ago one had to start from plain, rough material and work patiently for years to get the effect, whereas now the material doesn't matter at all, and with any sort of scrap, treated in the gas furnace under tremendous pressure, one may make a figure of colossal size like the one in Central Square.

So naturally Central Square with its trees and its fountains and its statues is one of the places of chief interest in the City.   But especially because there stands along one side of it the vast pile of the Grand Palaver Hotel.   It rises fifteen stories high and fills all one side of the square.   It has, overlooking the trees in the square, twelve hundred rooms with three thousand windows, and it would have held all George Washington's army.   Even people in other cities who have never seen it know it well from its advertising; "the most homelike hotel in America," so it is labelled in all the magazines, the expensive ones, on the continent.   In fact, the aim of the company that owns the Grand Palaver—and they do not attempt to conceal it— is to make the place as much a home as possible.   Therein lies its charm.   It is a home.   You realise that when you look up at the Grand Palaver from the square at night when the twelve hundred guests have turned on the lights of the three thousand windows.   You realise it at theatre time when the great strings of motors come sweeping to the doors of the Palaver, to carry the twelve hundred guests to twelve hundred seats in the theatres at four dollars a seat.   But most of all do you appreciate the character of the Grand Palaver when you step into its rotunda. Aladdin's enchanted palace was nothing to it.   It has a vast ceiling with a hundred glittering lights, and within it night and day is a surging crowd that is never still and a babel of voices that is never hushed, and over all there hangs an enchanted cloud of thin blue tobacco smoke such as might enshroud the conjured vision of a magician of Bagdad or Damascus.

In and through the rotunda there are palm-trees to rest the eye and rubber-trees in boxes to soothe the mind, and there are great leather lounges and deep arm-chairs, and here and there huge brass ash-bowls as big as Etruscan tear-jugs. Along one side is a counter with grated wickets like a bank, and behind it are five clerks with flattened hair and tall collars, dressed in long black frock-coats all day like members of a legislature. They have great books in front of them in which they study unceasingly, and at their lightest thought they strike a bell with the open palm of their hand, and at the sound of it a page boy in a monkey suit, with G. P. stamped all over him in brass, bounds to the desk and off again, shouting a call into the unheeding crowd vociferously. The sound of it fills for a moment the great space of the rotunda; it echoes down the corridors to the side; it floats, softly melodious, through the palm-trees of the ladies' palm room; it is heard, fainter and fainter, in the distant grill, and in the depths of the barber shop below the level of the street the barber arrests a moment the drowsy hum of his shampoo brushes to catch the sound—as might a miner in the sunken galleries of a coastal mine cease in his toil a moment to hear the distant murmur of the sea.

And the clerks call for the pages, the pages call for the guests, and the guests call for the porters, the bells clang, the elevators rattle, till home itself was never half so home-like.

   .    .    .    .    .    .    .

"A call for Mr. Tomlinson! A call for Mr. Tomlinson!"

So went the sound, echoing through the rotunda.

And as the page boy found him and handed him on a salver a telegram to read, the eyes of the crowd about him turned for a moment to look upon the figure of Tomlinson, the Wizard of Finance.

There he stood in his wide-awake hat and his long black coat, his shoulders slightly bent with his fifty-eight years. Anyone who had known him in the olden days on his bush farm beside Tomlinson's Creek in the country of the Great Lakes would have recognised him in a moment. There was still on his face that strange, puzzled look that it habitually wore, only now, of course, the financial papers were calling it "unfathomable." There was a certain way in which his eye roved to and fro inquiringly that might have looked like perplexity, were it not that the *Financial Undertone* had recognised it as the "searching look of a captain of industry." One might have thought that for all the goodness in it there was something simple in his face, were it not that the *Commercial and Pictorial Review* had called the face "inscrutable," and had proved it so with an illustration that left no doubt of the matter. Indeed, the face of Tomlinson of Tomlinson's Creek, now Tomlinson the Wizard of Finance, was not commonly spoken of as a *face* by the paragraphers of the Saturday magazine sections, but was more usually referred to as a mask; and it would appear that Napoleon the First had had one also. The Saturday editors were never tired of describing the strange, impressive personality of Tomlinson, the great dominating character of the newest and highest finance. From the moment when the interim prospectus of the Erie Auriferous Consolidated had broken like a tidal wave over Stock Exchange circles, the picture of Tomlinson, the sleeping shareholder of uncomputed millions, had filled the imagination of every dreamer in a nation of poets.

They all described him. And when each had finished he began again.

"The face," so wrote the editor of the "Our Own Men" section of *Ourselves Monthly*, "is that of a typical American captain of finance, hard, yet with a certain softness, broad but with a certain length, ductile but not without its own firmness."

"The mouth," so wrote the editor of the "Success" column of *Brains*, "is strong but pliable, the jaw firm and yet movable, while there is something in the set of the ear that suggests the swift, eager mind of the born leader of men."

So from state to state ran the portrait of Tomlinson of Tomlinson's Creek, drawn by people who had never seen him; so did it reach out and cross the ocean, till the French journals inserted a picture which they used for such occasions, and called it *Monsieur Tomlinson, nouveau capitaine de la haute finance en Amérique;* and the German weeklies, inserting also a suitable picture from their stock, marked it *Herr Tomlinson, Amerikanischer Industrie und Finanzcapitän.* Thus did Tomlinson float from Tomlinson's Creek beside Lake Erie to the very banks of the Danube and the Drave.

Some writers grew lyric about him. What visions, they asked, could one but read them, must lie behind the quiet, dreaming eyes of that inscrutable face?

They might have read them easily enough, had they but had the key. Anyone who looked upon Tomlinson as he stood there in the roar and clatter of the great rotunda of the Grand Palaver with the telegram in his hand, fumbling at the wrong end to open it, might have read the visions of the master-mind had he but known their nature. They were simple enough. For the visions in the mind of Tomlinson, Wizard of Finance, were for the most part those of a wind-swept hillside farm beside Lake Erie, where Tomlinson's Creek runs down to the low edge of the lake, and where the off-shore wind ripples the rushes of the shallow water: that, and the vision of a frame house, and the snake fences of the fourth concession road where it falls to the lakeside. And if the eyes of the man are dreamy and abstracted, it is because there lies over the vision of this vanished farm an infinite regret, greater in its compass than all the shares the Erie Auriferous Consolidated has ever thrown upon the market.

．　　．　　．　　．　　．　　．　　．

When Tomlinson had opened the telegram he stood with it for a moment in his hand, looking the boy full in the face. His look had in it that peculiar far-away quality that the newspapers were calling "Napoleonic abstraction." In reality he was wondering whether to give the boy twenty-five cents or fifty.

The message that he had just read was worded, "Morning quotations show preferred A. G. falling rapidly recommend instant sale no confidence send instructions."

The Wizard of Finance took from his pocket a pencil (it was a carpenter's pencil) and wrote across the face of the message,

"Buy me quite a bit more of the same yours truly."

This he gave to the boy. "Take it over to him," he said, pointing to the telegraph corner of the rotunda. Then after another pause he mumbled, "Here, sonny," and gave the boy a dollar.

With that he turned to walk towards the elevator, and all the people about him who had watched the signing of the message knew that some big financial deal was going through—a *coup*, in fact, they called it.

The elevator took the Wizard to the second floor. As he went up he felt in his pocket and gripped a quarter, then changed his mind and felt for a fifty-cent piece, and finally gave them both to the elevator boy, after which he walked along the corridor till he reached the corner suite of rooms, a palace in itself, for which he was paying a thousand dollars a month ever since the Erie Auriferous Consolidated Company had begun tearing up the bed of Tomlinson's Creek in Cahoga County with its hydraulic dredges.

"Well, mother," he said as he entered.

There was a woman seated near the window, a woman with a plain, homely face such as they wear in the farm kitchens of Cahoga County, and a set of fashionable clothes upon her such as they sell to the ladies of Plutoria Avenue.

This was "mother," the wife of the Wizard of Finance and eight years younger than himself. And she too was in the papers and the public eye; and whatsoever the shops had fresh from Paris, at fabulous prices, that they sold to mother. They had put a Balkan hat upon her with an upright feather, and they had hung gold chains on her, and everything that was most expensive they had hung and tied on mother. You might see her emerging any morning from the Grand Palaver in her beetle-back jacket and her Balkan hat, a figure of infinite pathos. And whatever she wore, the lady editors of *Spring Notes* and *Causerie du Boudoir* wrote it out in French, and one paper had called her a *belle châtelaine*, and another had spoken of her as a *grande dame*, which the Tomlinsons thought must be a misprint.

But in any case, for Tomlinson the Wizard of Finance it was a great relief to have as his wife a woman like mother, because he knew that she had taught school in Cahoga County and could hold her own in the city with any of them.

So mother spent her time sitting in her beetle jacket in the thousand-dollar suite, reading new novels in brilliant paper covers. And the Wizard on his trips up and down to the rotunda brought her the very best, the ones that cost a dollar fifty, because he knew that out home she had only been able to read books like Nathaniel Hawthorne and Walter Scott, that were only worth ten cents.

. . . . . . . .

"How's Fred?" said the Wizard, laying aside his hat, and looking towards the closed door of an inner room. "Is he better?"

"Some," said mother. "He's dressed, but he's lying down."

Fred was the son of the Wizard and mother. In the inner room he lay on a sofa, a great hulking boy of seventeen in a flowered dressing-gown, fancying himself ill. There was a packet of cigarettes and a box of chocolates on a chair beside him, and he had the blind drawn and his eyes half-closed to impress himself.

Yet this was the same boy that less than a year ago on Tomlinson's Creek had worn a rough store suit and set his sturdy shoulders to the buck-saw. At present Fortune was busy taking from him the golden gifts which the fairies of Cahoga County, Lake Erie, had laid in his cradle seventeen years ago.

The Wizard tip-toed into the inner room, and from the open door his listening wife could hear the voice of the boy saying, in a tone as of one distraught with suffering:

"Is there any more of that jelly?"

"Could he have any, do you suppose?" asked Tomlinson, coming back.

"It's all right," said mother, "if it will sit on his stomach."

For this, in the dietetics of Cahoga County, is the sole test. All those things can be eaten which will sit on the stomach. Anything that won't sit there is not eatable.

"Do you suppose I could get them to get any?" questioned Tomlinson. "Would it be all right to telephone down to the office, or do you think it would be better to ring?"

"Perhaps," said his wife, "it would be better to look

out into the hall and see if there isn't someone round that would tell them."

This was the kind of problem with which Tomlinson and his wife, in their thousand-dollar suite in the Grand Palaver, grappled all day. And when presently a tall waiter in dress-clothes appeared, and said, "Jelly? Yes, sir, immediately, sir; would you like, sir, Maraschino, sir, or Portovino, sir?" Tomlinson gazed at him gloomily, wondering if he would take five dollars.

"What does the doctor say is wrong with Fred?" asked Tomlinson, when the waiter had gone.

"He don't just say," said mother; "he said he must keep very quiet. He looked in this morning for a minute or two, and he said he'd look in later in the day again. But he said to keep Fred very quiet."

Exactly! In other words Fred had pretty much the same complaint as the rest of Dr. Slyder's patients on Plutoria Avenue, and was to be treated in the same way. Dr. Slyder, who was the most fashionable practitioner in the City, spent his entire time moving to and fro in an almost noiseless motor earnestly advising people to keep quiet. "You must keep very quiet for a little while," he would say with a sigh, as he sat beside a sick-bed. As he drew on his gloves in the hall below he would shake his head very impressively and say, "You must keep him very quiet," and so pass out, quite soundlessly. By this means Dr. Slyder often succeeded in keeping people quiet for weeks. It was all the medicine that he knew. But it was enough. And as his patients always got well—there being nothing wrong with them—his reputation was immense.

Very naturally the Wizard and his wife were impressed with him. They had never seen such therapeutics in Cahoga County, where the practice of medicine is carried on with forceps, pumps, squirts, splints, and other instruments of violence.

The waiter had hardly gone when a boy appeared at the door. This time he presented to Tomlinson not one telegram but a little bundle of them.

The Wizard read them with a lengthening face. The first ran something like this, "Congratulate you on your daring market turned instantly"; and the next, "Your opinion justified market rose have sold at 20 points profit"; and a third, "Your forecast entirely correct C. P. rose at once send further instructions."

These and similar messages were from brokers' offices, and all of them were in the same tone; one told him that C. P. was up, and another T. G. P. had passed 129, and another that T. C. R. R. had risen ten—all of which things were imputed to the wonderful sagacity of Tomlinson. Whereas if they had told him that X. Y. Z. had risen to the moon he would have been just as wise as to what it meant.

"Well," said the wife of the Wizard as her husband finished looking through the reports, "how are things this morning? Are they any better?"

"No," said Tomlinson, and he sighed as he said it; "this is the worst day yet. It's just been a shower of telegrams, and mostly all the same. I can't do the figuring of it like you can, but I reckon I must have made another hundred thousand dollars since yesterday."

"You don't say so!" said mother, and they looked at one another gloomily.

"And half a million last week, wasn't it?" said Tomlinson as he sank into a chair. "I'm afraid, mother," he continued, "it's no good. We don't know how. We weren't brought up to it."

All of which meant that if the editor of the *Monetary*

*Afternoon* or *Financial Sunday* had been able to know what was happening with the two wizards, he could have written up a news story calculated to electrify all America.

For the truth was that Tomlinson, the Wizard of Finance, was attempting to carry out a *coup* greater than any as yet attributed to him by the Press. He was trying to lose his money. That, in the sickness of his soul, crushed by the Grand Palaver, overwhelmed with the burden of high finance, had become his aim, to be done with it, to get rid of his whole fortune.

But if you own a fortune that is computed anywhere from fifty millions up, with no limit at the top, if you own one-half of all the preferred stock of an Erie Auriferous Consolidated that is digging gold in hydraulic bucketfuls from a quarter of a mile of river bed, the task of losing it is no easy matter.

There are men, no doubt, versed in finance, who might succeed in doing it. But they have a training that Tomlinson lacked. Invest it as he would in the worst securities that offered, the most rickety of stock, the most fraudulent bonds, back it came to him. When he threw a handful away, back came two in its place. And at every new *coup* the crowd applauded the incomparable daring, the unparalleled prescience of the Wizard.

Like the touch of Midas, his hand turned everything to gold.

"Mother," he repeated, "it's no use. It's like this here Destiny, as the books call it."

.    .    .    .    .    .    .

The great fortune that Tomlinson, the Wizard of Finance, was trying his best to lose had come to him with wonderful suddenness. As yet it was hardly six months old. As to how it had originated, there were all sorts of stories afloat in the weekly illustrated press. They agreed mostly on the general basis that Tomlinson had made his vast fortune by his own indomitable pluck and dogged industry. Some said that he had been at one time a mere farm hand who, by sheer doggedness, had fought his way from the hay-mow to the control of the produce market of seventeen states. Others had it that he had been a lumber-jack who, by sheer doggedness, had got possession of the whole lumber forest of the Lake district. Others said that he had been a miner in a Lake Superior copper mine who had, by the doggedness of his character, got a practical monopoly of the copper supply. These Saturday articles, at any rate, made the Saturday reader rigid with sympathetic doggedness himself, which was all that the editor (who was doggedly trying to make the paper pay) wanted to effect.

But in reality the making of Tomlinson's fortune was very simple. The recipe for it is open to anyone. It is only necessary to own a hillside farm beside Lake Erie where the uncleared bush and the broken fields go straggling down to the lake, and to have running through it a creek, such as that called Tomlinson's, brawling among the stones and willows, and to discover in the bed of a creek—a gold mine.

That is all.

Nor is it necessary in these well-ordered days to discover the gold for one's self. One might have lived a lifetime on the farm, as Tomlinson's father had, and never discover it for one's self. For that indeed the best medium of destiny is a geologist, let us say the senior professor of geology at Plutoria University.

That was how it happened.

The senior professor, so it chanced, was spending his vacation near by on the shores of the lake, and his time was mostly passed—for how better can a man spend a month of pleasure?—in looking for outcroppings of Devonian rock of the post-tertiary period.  For which purpose he carried a vacation hammer in his pocket, and made from time to time a note or two as he went along, or filled his pockets with the chippings of vacation rocks.

So it chanced that he came to Tomlinson's Creek at the very point where a great slab of Devonian rock bursts through the clay of the bank.  When the senior professor of geology saw it and noticed a stripe like a mark on a tiger's back—a fault he called it—that ran over the face of the block, he was at it in an instant, beating off fragments with his little hammer.

Tomlinson and his boy Fred were logging in the underbrush near by with a long chain and yoke of oxen, but the geologist was so excited that he did not see them till the sound of his eager hammer had brought them to his side. They took him up to the frame house in the clearing, where the chatelaine was hoeing a potato patch with a man's hat on her head, and they gave him buttermilk and soda cakes, but his hand shook so that he could hardly eat them.

The geologist left Cahoga station that night for the City with a newspaper full of specimens inside his suitcase, and he knew that if any person or persons would put up money enough to tear that block of rock away and follow the fissure down, there would be found there something to astonish humanity, geologists and all.

.    .    .    .    .    .    .

After that point in the launching of a gold mine the rest is easy.  Generous, warm-hearted men, interested in geology, were soon found.  There was no stint of money. The great rock was torn sideways from its place, and from beneath it the crumbled, glittering rock-dust that sparkled in the sun was sent in little boxes to the testing laboratories of Plutoria University. There the senior professor of geology had sat up with it far into the night in a darkened laboratory, with little blue flames playing underneath crucibles, as in a magician's cavern, and with the door locked. And as each sample that he tested was set aside and tied in a cardboard box by itself, he labelled it "aur. p. 75," and the pen shook in his hand as he marked it. For to professors of geology those symbols mean "this is seventy-five per cent pure gold." So it was no wonder that the senior professor of geology working far into the night among the blue flames shook with excitement; not, of course, for the gold's sake as money (he had no time to think of that), but because if this thing was true it meant that an auriferous vein had been found in what was Devonian rock of the post-tertiary stratification, and if that was so it upset enough geology to spoil a textbook. It would mean that the professor could read a paper at the next Pan-Geological Conference that would turn the whole assembly into a bedlam.

It pleased him, too, to know that the men he was dealing with were generous. They had asked him to name his own price for the tests that he made, and when he had said two dollars per sample they had told him to go right ahead. The professor was not, I suppose, a mercenary man, but it pleased him to think that he could clean up sixteen dollars in a single evening in his laboratory. It showed, at any rate, that business men put science at its proper value. Strangest of all was the fact that the men had told him that even this ore was apparently nothing to what there was; it had all come out of one single spot in the creek, not the hundredth part of the whole claim. Lower down, where they had thrown the big dam across to make the bed dry, they were taking out this same stuff and even better, so they said, in cartloads.  The hydraulic dredges were tearing it from the bed of the creek all day, and at night a great circuit of arc lights gleamed and sputtered over the roaring labour of the friends of geological research.

Thus had the Erie Auriferous Consolidated broken in a tidal wave over financial circles.  On the Stock Exchange, in the down-town offices, and among the palm-trees of the Mausoleum Club they talked of nothing else.  And so great was the power of the wave that it washed Tomlinson and his wife along on the crest of it, and landed them fifty feet up in their thousand-dollar suite in the Grand Palaver.  And as a result of it "mother" wore a beetle-back jacket, and Tomlinson received a hundred telegrams a day, and Fred quit school and ate chocolates.

But in the business world the most amazing thing about it was the wonderful shrewdness of Tomlinson.

The first sign of it had been that he had utterly refused to allow the Erie Auriferous Consolidated (as the friends of geology called themselves) to take over the top half of the Tomlinson farm.  For the bottom part he let them give him one-half of the preferred stock in the company in return for their supply of development capital.  This was their own proposition; in fact, they reckoned that in doing this they were trading about two hundred thousand dollars' worth of machinery for, say ten million dollars of gold.  But it frightened them when Tomlinson said "Yes" to the offer, and when he said that as to common stock they might keep it, it was no use to him, they were alarmed and uneasy till they made him take a block of it for the sake of market confidence.

But the top end of the farm he refused to surrender, and the friends of applied geology knew that there must be something pretty large behind this refusal; the more so as the reason that Tomlinson gave was such a simple one. He said that he didn't want to part with the top end of the place because his father was buried on it beside the creek, and so he didn't want the dam higher up, not for any consideration.

This was regarded in business circles as a piece of great shrewdness. "Says his father is buried there, eh? Devilish shrewd that!"

It was so long since any of the members of the Exchange or the Mausoleum Club had wandered into such places as Cahoga County that they did not know that there was nothing strange in what Tomlinson said. His father was buried there, on the farm itself, in a grave overgrown with raspberry bushes, and with a wooden headstone encompassed by a square of cedar rails, and slept as many another pioneer of Cahoga is sleeping.

"Devilish smart idea!" they said; and forthwith half the financial men of the city buried their fathers, or professed to have done so, in likely places—along the prospective right-of-way of a suburban railway, for example; in fact, in any place that marked them out for the joyous resurrection of an expropriation purchase.

Thus the astounding shrewdness of Tomlinson rapidly became a legend, the more so as he turned everything he touched to gold.

They narrated little stories of him in the whiskey-and-soda corners of the Mausoleum Club.

"I put it to him in a casual way," related, for example, Mr. Lucullus Fyshe, "casually, but quite frankly. I said, 'See here, this is just a bagatelle to you, no doubt, but to me it might be of some use. T. C. bonds,' I said, 'have risen twenty-two and a half in a week. You know as well as I do that they are only collateral trust, and that the stock underneath never could and never can earn a par dividend. Now,' I said, 'Mr. Tomlinson, tell me what all that means?' Would you believe it, the fellow looked me right in the face in that queer way he has and he said, 'I don't know!' "

"He said he didn't know!" repeated the listener, in a tone of amazement and respect. "By Jove! eh? he said he didn't know! The man's a wizard!"

"And he looked as if he didn't!" went on Mr. Fyshe. "That's the deuce of it. That man when he wants to can put on a look, sir, that simply means nothing, absolutely nothing."

In this way Tomlinson had earned his name of the Wizard of American Finance.

And meantime Tomlinson and his wife, within their suite at the Grand Palaver, had long since reached their decision. For there was one aspect and only one in which Tomlinson was really and truly a wizard. He saw clearly that for himself and his wife the vast fortune that had fallen to them was of no manner of use. What did it bring them? The noise and roar of the City in place of the silence of the farm and the racket of the great rotunda to drown the remembered murmur of the waters of the creek.

So Tomlinson had decided to rid himself of his new wealth, save only such as might be needed to make his son a different kind of man from himself.

"For Fred, of course," he said, "it's different. But out of such a lot as that it'll be easy to keep enough for him. It'll be a grand thing for Fred, this money. He won't have to grow up like you and me. He'll have opportunities we never got."

He was getting them already. The opportunity to wear seven-dollar patent leather shoes and a bell-shaped overcoat with a silk collar, to lounge into moving picture shows and eat chocolates and smoke cigarettes—all these opportunities he was gathering immediately. Presently, when he learned his way round a little, he would get still bigger ones.

"He's improving fast," said mother. She was thinking of his patent leather shoes.

"He's popular," said his father. "I notice it downstairs. He sasses any of them just as he likes; and no matter how busy they are, as soon as they see it's Fred they're all ready to have a laugh with him."

Certainly they were, as any hotel clerk with plastered hair is ready to laugh with the son of a multimillionaire. It's a certain sense of humour that they develop.

"But for us, mother," said the Wizard, "we'll be rid of it. The gold is there. It's not right to keep it back. But we'll just find a way to pass it on to folks that need it worse than we do."

For a time they had thought of giving away the fortune. But how? Who did they know that would take it?

It had crossed their minds—for who could live in the City a month without observing the imposing buildings of Plutoria University, as fine as any departmental store in town?—that they might give it to the college.

But there, it seemed, the way was blocked.

"You see, mother," said the puzzled Wizard, "we're not known. We're strangers. I'd look fine going up there to the college and saying, 'I want to give you people a million dollars.' They'd laugh at me!"

"But don't one read it in the papers," his wife had protested, "where Mr. Carnegie gives ever so much to the colleges, more than all we've got, and they take it?"

"That's different," said the Wizard. "He's in with them. They all know him. Why, he's a sort of chairman of different boards of colleges, and he knows all the heads of the schools, and the professors, so it's no wonder that if he offers to give a pension, or anything, they take it. Just think of me going up to one of the professors up there in the middle of his teaching and saying, 'I'd like to give you a pension for life!' Imagine it! Think what he'd say!"

But the Tomlinsons couldn't imagine it, which was just as well.

So it came about that they had embarked on their system. Mother, who knew most arithmetic, was the leading spirit. She tracked out all the stocks and bonds in the front page of the *Financial Undertone*, and on her recommendation the Wizard bought. They knew the stocks only by their letters, but this itself gave a touch of high finance to their deliberations.

"I'd buy some of this R. O. P. if I was you," said mother; "it's gone down from 127 to 107 in two days, and I reckon it'll be all gone in ten days or so."

"Wouldn't 'G. G. deb.' be better? It goes down quicker."

"Well, it's a quick one," she assented, "but it don't go down so steady. You can't rely on it. You take ones like R. O. P. and T. R. R. pfd.; they go down all the time and you know where you are."

As a result of which Tomlinson would send his instructions. He did it all from the rotunda in a way of his own that he had evolved with a telegraph clerk who told him the names of brokers, and he dealt thus through brokers whom he never saw. As a result of this, the sluggish R. O. P. and T. R. R. would take as sudden a leap into the air as might a mule with a galvanic shock applied to its tail. At once the word was whispered that the "Tomlinson interests" were after the R. O. P. to reorganise it, and the whole floor of the Exchange scrambled for the stock.

And so it was that after a month or two of these

operations the Wizard of Finance saw himself beaten.

"It's no good, mother," he repeated, "it's just a kind of Destiny."

Destiny perhaps it was.

But, if the Wizard of Finance had known it, at this very moment when he sat with the Aladdin's palace of his golden fortune reared so strangely about him, Destiny was preparing for him still stranger things.

Destiny, so it would seem, was devising its own ways and means of dealing with Tomlinson's fortune. As one of the ways and means, Destiny was sending at this moment as its special emissaries two huge, portly figures, wearing gigantic goloshes, and striding downwards from the halls of Plutoria University to the Grand Palaver Hotel. And one of these was the gigantic Dr. Boomer, the president of the college, and the other was his professor of Greek, almost as gigantic as himself. And they carried in their capacious pockets bundles of pamphlets on "Archæological Remains of Mitylene," and the "Use of the Greek Pluperfect," and little treatises such as "Education and Philanthropy," by Dr. Boomer, and "The Excavation of Mitylene: An Estimate of Cost," by Dr. Boyster, "Boomer on the Foundation and Maintenance of Chairs," etc.

Many a man in city finance who had seen Dr. Boomer enter his office with a bundle of these monographs and a fighting glitter in his eyes had sunk back in his chair in dismay. For it meant that Dr. Boomer had tracked him out for a benefaction to the University, and that all resistance was hopeless.

When Dr. Boomer once laid upon a capitalist's desk his famous pamphlet on the "Use of the Greek Pluperfect," it was as if an Arabian sultan had sent the fatal bow-string to a condemned pasha, or Morgan the buccaneer had served the death-sign on a shuddering pirate.

So they came nearer and nearer, shouldering the passers-by. The sound of them as they talked was like the roaring of the sea as Homer heard it. Never did Castor and Pollux come surging into battle as Dr. Boomer and Dr. Boyster bore down upon the Grand Palaver Hotel.

Tomlinson, the Wizard of Finance, had hesitated about going to the University. The University was coming to him. As for those millions of his, he could take his choice —dormitories, apparatus, campuses, buildings, endowment, anything he liked—but choose he must. And if he feared that after all his fortune was too vast even for such a disposal, Dr. Boomer would show him how he might use it in digging up ancient Mitylene, or modern Smyrna, or the lost cities of the Plain of Pactolus. If the size of the fortune troubled him Dr. Boomer would dig him up the whole African Sahara from Alexandria to Morocco, and ask for more.

But if Destiny held all this for Tomlinson in its out-stretched palm before it, it concealed stranger things still beneath the folds of its toga.

There were enough surprises there to turn the faces of the whole directorate of the Erie Auriferous Consolidated as yellow as the gold that they mined.

For at this very moment, while the president of Plutoria University drew nearer and nearer to the Grand Palaver Hotel, the senior professor of geology was working again beside the blue flames in his darkened laboratory. And this time there was no shaking excitement over him. Nor were the labels that he marked, as sample followed sample in the tests, the same as those of the previous marking. Not by any means.

And his grave face as he worked in silence was as still as the stones of the post-tertiary period.

# The Arrested Philanthropy of Mr. Tomlinson

"THIS, Mr. Tomlinson, is our campus," said President Boomer as they passed through the iron gates of Plutoria University.

"For camping?" said the Wizard.

"Not exactly," answered the president, "though it would, of course, suit for that. *Nihil humanum alienum,* eh?" and he broke into a loud, explosive laugh, while his spectacles irradiated that peculiar form of glee derived from a Latin quotation by those able to enjoy it. Dr. Boyster, walking on the other side of Mr. Tomlinson, joined in the laugh in a deep, reverberating chorus.

The two had the Wizard of Finance between them, and they were marching him up to the University. He was taken along much as is an arrested man who has promised to go quietly. They kept their hands off him, but they watched him sideways through their spectacles. At the least sign of restlessness they doused him with Latin. The Wizard of Finance, having been marked out by Dr. Boomer and Dr. Boyster as a prospective benefactor, was having Latin poured over him to reduce him to the proper degree of plasticity.

They had already put him through the first stage. They had, three days ago, called on him at the Grand Palaver and served him with a pamphlet on "The Excavation of Mitylene" as a sort of writ. Tomlinson and his wife had looked at the pictures of the ruins, and from the appearance of them they judged that Mitylene was in Mexico,

264

and they said that it was a shame to see it in that state and that the United States ought to intervene.

As the second stage on the path of philanthropy, the Wizard of Finance was now being taken to look at the university. Dr. Boomer knew by experience that no rich man could look at it without wanting to give it money.

And here the president had found that there is no better method of dealing with business men than to use Latin on them. For other purposes the president used other things. For example at a friendly dinner at the Mausoleum Club where light conversation was in order, Dr. Boomer chatted, as has been seen, on the archæological remains of the Navajos. In the same way, at Mrs. Rasselyer-Brown's Dante luncheons, he generally talked of the Italian *cinquecentisti* and whether Gian Gobbo della Scala had left a greater name than Can Grande della Spiggiola. But such talk as that was naturally only for women. Business men are much too shrewd for that kind of thing; in fact, so shrewd are they, as President Boomer had long since discovered, that nothing pleases them so much as the quiet, firm assumption that they know Latin. It is like writing them up an asset. So it was that Dr. Boomer would greet a business acquaintance with a roaring salutation of, *"Terque quaterque beatus,"* or stand wringing his hand off to the tune of *"Oh et presidium et dulce decus meum."*

This caught them every time.

"You don't," said Tomlinson the Wizard in a hesitating tone as he looked at the smooth grass of the campus, "I suppose, raise anything on it?"

"No, no; this is only for field sports," said the president; *"sunt quos curriculo—"*

To which Dr. Boyster on the other side added, like a chorus, *"pulverem Olympicum."*

This was their favourite quotation. It always gave

President Boomer a chance to speak of the final letter "m" in Latin poetry, and to say that in his opinion the so-called elision of the final "m" was more properly a dropping of the vowel with a repercussion of the two last consonants. He supported this by quoting Ammianus, at which Dr. Boyster exclaimed, "Pooh!   Ammianus: more dog Latin!" and appealed to Mr. Tomlinson as to whether any rational man nowadays cared what Ammianus thought?

To all of which Tomlinson answered never a word, but looked steadily first at one and then at the other. Dr. Boomer said afterwards that the penetration of Tomlinson was wonderful, and that it was excellent to see how Boyster tried in vain to draw him; and Boyster said afterwards that the way in which Tomlinson quietly refused to be led on by Boomer was delicious, and that it was a pity that Aristophanes was not there to do it justice.

All of which was happening as they went in at the iron gates and up the elm avenue of Plutoria University.

The university, as everyone knows, stands with its great gates on Plutoria Avenue, and with its largest buildings, those of the faculties of industrial and mechanical science, fronting full upon the street.

These buildings are exceptionally fine, standing fifteen stories high and comparing favourably with the best departmental stores or factories in the City. Indeed, after nightfall, when they are all lighted up for the evening technical classes and when their testing machinery is in full swing and there are students going in and out in overall suits, people have often mistaken the university, or this newer part of it, for a factory.   A foreign visitor once said that the students looked like plumbers, and President Boomer was so proud of it that he put the phrase into his next Commencement address; and from there the newspapers got it and the Associated Press took it up and sent it all over the United States with the heading, "Have Appearance of Plumbers; Plutoria University Congratulated on Character of Students," and it was a proud day indeed for the heads of the Industrial Science faculty.

But the older part of the university stands so quietly and modestly at the top end of the elm avenue, so hidden by the leaves of it, that no one could mistake it for a factory. This indeed was once the whole university, and had stood there since colonial days under the name Concordia College. It had been filled with generations of presidents and professors of the older type with long white beards and rusty black clothes, and salaries of fifteen hundred dollars.

But the change both of name and of character from Concordia College to Plutoria University was the work of President Boomer. He had changed it from an old-fashioned college of the by-gone type to a university in the true modern sense. At Plutoria they now taught everything. Concordia College, for example, had no teaching of religion except lectures on the Bible. Now they had lectures also on Confucianism, Mohammedanism, Buddhism, with an optional course on atheism for students in the final year.

And, of course, they had long since admitted women, and there were now beautiful creatures with Cléo de Mérode hair studying astronomy at oaken desks and looking up at the teacher with eyes like comets. The university taught everything and did everything. It had whirling machines on the top of it that measured the speed of the wind, and deep in its basements it measured earthquakes with a seismograph; it held classes on forestry and dentistry and palmistry; it sent life classes into the slums, and death classes to the city morgue. It offered such a vast variety of themes, topics, and subjects to the students, that there was nothing that a student was compelled to learn, while from its own presses in its own press-building it sent out a shower of bulletins and monographs like driven snow from a rotary plough.

In fact, it had become, as President Boomer told all the business men in town, not merely a university, but a *universitas* in the true sense, and every one of its faculties was now a *facultas* in the real acceptance of the word, and its studies properly and truly *studia;* indeed, if the business men would only build a few more dormitories and put up enough money to form an adequate *fondatum* or *fundum* then the good work might be looked upon as complete.

As the three walked up the elm avenue there met them a little stream of students with college books, and female students with winged-victory hats, and professors with last year's overcoats. And some went past with a smile and others with a shiver.

"That's Professor Withers," said the president in a sympathetic voice as one of the shivering figures went past; "poor Withers," and he sighed.

"What's wrong with him?" said the Wizard; "is he sick?"

"No, not sick," said the president quietly and sadly, "merely inefficient."

"Inefficient?"

"Unfortunately so. Mind you, I don't mean 'inefficient' in every sense. By no means. If anyone were to come to me and say, 'Boomer, can you put your hand for me on a first-class botanist?' I'd say, 'Take Withers.' I'd say it in a minute."

This was true. He would have. In fact, if anyone had made this kind of rash speech, Dr. Boomer would have given away half the professoriate.

"Well, what's wrong with him?" repeated Tomlinson.

"I suppose he ain't quite up to the mark in some ways, eh?"

"Precisely," said the president, "not quite up to the mark—a very happy way of putting it. *Capax imperii nisi imperasset,* as no doubt you are thinking to yourself. The fact is that Withers, though an excellent fellow, can't manage large classes. With small classes he is all right, but with large classes the man is lost. He can't handle them."

"He can't, eh?" said the Wizard.

"No. But what can I do? There he is. I can't dismiss him, I can't pension him. I've no money for it."

Here the president slackened a little in his walk and looked sideways at the prospective benefactor. But Tomlinson gave no sign.

A second professorial figure passed them on the other side.

"There again," said the president, "that's another case of inefficiency—Professor Shottat, our senior professor of English."

"What's wrong with *him?*" asked the Wizard.

"He can't handle *small* classes," said the president. "With large classes he is really excellent, but with small ones the man is simply hopeless."

In this fashion, before Mr. Tomlinson had measured the length of the avenue, he had had ample opportunity to judge of the crying need of money at Plutoria University, and of the perplexity of its president. He was shown professors who could handle the first year, but were powerless with the second; others who were all right with the second but broke down with the third, while others could handle the third but collapsed with the fourth. There were professors who were all right in their own subject, but perfectly impossible outside of it; others who were so occupied outside of their own subject that they were useless inside of it; others who knew their subject, but couldn't lecture; and others again who lectured admirably, but didn't know their subject.

In short it was clear—as it was meant to be—that the need of the moment was a sum of money sufficient to enable the president to dismiss everybody but himself and Dr. Boyster. The latter stood in a class all by himself. He had known the president for forty-five years, ever since he was a fat little boy with spectacles in a classical academy, stuffing himself on irregular Greek verbs as readily as if on oysters.

But it soon appeared that the need for dismissing the professors was only part of the trouble. There were the buildings to consider.

"This, I am ashamed to say," said Dr. Boomer, as they passed the imitation Greek portico of the old Concordia College building, "is our original home, the *fons et origo* of our studies, our faculty of arts."

It was indeed a dilapidated building, yet there was a certain majesty about it, too, especially when one reflected that it had been standing there looking much the same at the time when its students had trooped off in a flock to join the army of the Potomac, and much the same indeed three generations before that, when the classes were closed and the students clapped three-cornered hats on their heads and were off to enlist as minute men with flintlock muskets under General Washington.

But Dr. Boomer's one idea was to knock the building down and to build on its site a real *facultas* ten stories high, with elevators in it.

Tomlinson looked about him humbly as he stood in the main hall. The atmosphere of the place awed him. There were bulletins and time-tables and notices stuck on the walls that gave evidence of the activity of the place.

"Professor Slithers will be unable to meet his classes to-day," ran one of them, and another, "Professor Withers will not meet his classes this week," and another, "Owing to illness, Professor Shottat will not lecture this month," while still another announced, "Owing to the indisposition of Professor Podge, all botanical classes are suspended, but Professor Podge hopes to be able to join in the Botanical Picnic Excursion to Loon Lake on Saturday afternoon." You could judge of the grinding routine of the work from the nature of these notices. Anyone familiar with the work of colleges would not heed it, but it shocked Tomlinson to think how often the professors of the college were stricken down by overwork.

Here and there in the hall, set into niches, were bronze busts of men with Roman faces and bare necks, and the edge of a toga cast over each shoulder.

"Who would these be?" asked Tomlinson, pointing at them.

"Some of the chief founders and benefactors of the faculty," answered the president, and at this the hopes of Tomlinson sank in his heart. For he realised the class of man one had to belong to in order to be accepted as a university benefactor.

"A splendid group of men, are they not?" said the president. "We owe them much. This is the late Mr. Hogworth, a man of singularly large heart." Here he pointed to a bronze figure wearing a wreath of laurel and inscribed "Gulielmus Hogworth, Litt. Doc." "He had made a great fortune in the produce business, and wishing to mark his gratitude to the community, he erected the anemometer, the wind-measure, on the roof of the building, attaching to it no other condition than that his name should be printed in the weekly reports immediately beside the velocity of the wind. The figure beside him is

Dr. Boyster were gravely discussing on what terms and in what way Fred might be admitted to study in the faculty of industrial science.   The president, on learning that Fred had put in four years in Cahoga County Section No. 3 School, and had been head of his class in ciphering, nodded his head gravely and said it would simply be a matter of a *pro tanto;* that, in fact, he felt sure that Fred might be admitted *ad eundem.*   But the real condition on which they meant to admit him was, of course, not mentioned.

One door only in the faculty of industrial and mechanical science they did not pass, a heavy oak door at the end of a corridor bearing the painted inscription, "Geological and Metallurgical Laboratories."   Stuck in the door was a card with the words (they were conceived in the courteous phrases of mechanical science, which is almost a branch of business in the real sense), "Busy—keep out."

Dr. Boomer looked at the card.   "Ah, yes," he said, "Gildas is no doubt busy with his tests.   We won't disturb him."   The president was always proud to find a professor busy; it looked well.

But if Dr. Boomer had known what was going on behind the oaken door of the Department of Geology and Metallurgy, he would have felt considerably disturbed himself.

For here again Gildas, senior professor of geology, was working among his blue flames at a final test on which depended the fate of the Erie Auriferous Consolidated and all connected with it.

Before him there were some twenty or thirty packets of crumpled dust and splintered ore that glittered on the testing table.   It had been taken up from the creek along its whole length, at even spaces twenty yards apart, by an expert sent down in haste by the directorate, after Gildas's second report, and heavily bribed to keep his mouth shut.

And as Professor Gildas stood and worked at the samples and tied them up after analysis in little white cardboard boxes, he marked each one very carefully and neatly with the words, "Pyrites: worthless."

Beside the professor worked a young demonstrator of last year's graduation class. It was he, in fact, who had written the polite notice on the card.

"What is the stuff, anyway?" he asked.

"A sulphuret of iron," said the professor, "or iron pyrites. In colour and appearance it is practically identical with gold. Indeed, in all ages," he went on, dropping at once into the class-room tone and adopting the professorial habit of jumping backwards twenty centuries in order to explain anything properly, "it has been readily mistaken for the precious metal. The ancients called it 'fool's gold.' Martin Frobisher brought back four shiploads of it from Baffin Land thinking that he had discovered an Eldorado. There are large deposits of it in the mines of Cornwall, and it is just possible," here the professor measured his words as if speaking of something that he wouldn't promise, "that the Cassiterides of the Phœnicians contained deposits of the same sulphuret. Indeed, I defy anyone," he continued, for he was piqued in his scientific pride, "to distinguish it from gold without a laboratory test. In large quantities, I concede, its lack of weight would betray it to a trained hand, but without testing its solubility in nitric acid, or the fact of its burning with a blue flame under the blow-pipe, it cannot be detected. In short, when crystallised in dodecahedrons—"

"Is it any good?" broke in the demonstrator.

"Good?" said the professor. "Oh, you mean commercially? Not in the slightest. Much less valuable than, let us say, ordinary mud or clay. In fact, it is absolutely good for nothing."

They were silent for a moment, watching the blue flames above the brazier.

Then Gildas spoke again. "Oddly enough," he said, "the first set of samples were undoubtedly pure gold—not the faintest doubt of that. That is the really interesting part of the matter. These gentlemen concerned in the enterprise will, of course, lose their money, and I shall therefore decline to accept the very handsome fee which they had offered me for my services. But the main feature, the real point of interest in this matter remains. Here we have undoubtedly a sporadic deposit,—what miners call a pocket,—of pure gold in a Devonian formation of the post-tertiary period. This once established, we must revise our entire theory of the distribution of igneous and aqueous rocks. In fact, I am already getting notes together for a paper for the Pan-Geological under the heading, 'Auriferous Excretions in the Devonian Strata: a Working Hypothesis.' I hope to read it at the next meeting."

The young demonstrator looked at the professor with one eye half closed.

"I don't think I would if I were you," he said.

Now this young demonstrator knew nothing, or practically nothing, of geology, because he came of one of the richest and best families in town and didn't need to. But he was a smart young man, dressed in the latest fashion, with brown boots and a crosswise tie, and he knew more about money and business and the Stock Exchange in five minutes than Professor Gildas in his whole existence.

"Why not?" said the professor.

"Why, don't you see what's happened?"

"Eh?" said Gildas.

"What happened to those first samples? When that bunch got interested and planned to float the company? Don't you see? Somebody salted them on you."

"*Salted* them on me?" repeated the professor, mystified.

"Yes, salted them.  Somebody got wise to what they were and swopped them on you for the real thing, so as to get your certified report that the stuff was gold."

"I begin to see," muttered the professor.  "Somebody exchanged the samples, some person no doubt desirous of establishing the theory that a sporadic outcropping of the sort might be found in a post-tertiary formation.  I see, I see.  No doubt he intended to prepare a paper on it, and prove his thesis by these tests.  I see it all!"

The demonstrator looked at the professor with a sort of pity.

"You're on!" he said, and he laughed softly to himself.

.      .      .      .      .      .      .

"Well," said Dr. Boomer, after Tomlinson had left the university, "what do you make of him?"  The president had taken Dr. Boyster over to his house beside the campus, and there in his study had given him a cigar as big as a rope and taken another himself.  This was a sign that Dr. Boomer wanted Dr. Boyster's opinion in plain English, without any Latin about it.

"Remarkable man," said the professor of Greek; "wonderful penetration, and a man of very few words.  Of course his game is clear enough?"

"Entirely so," asserted Dr. Boomer.

"It's clear enough that he means to give the money on two conditions."

"Exactly," said the president.

"First that we admit his son, who is quite unqualified, to the senior studies in electrical science, and second that we grant him the degree of Doctor of Letters.  Those are his terms."

"Can we meet them?"

"Oh, certainly.  As to the son, there is no difficulty, of

course; as to the degree, it's only a question of getting the faculty to vote it. I think we can manage it."

Vote it they did that very afternoon. True, if the members of the faculty had known the things that were being whispered, and more than whispered, in the City about Tomlinson and his fortune, no degree would ever have been conferred on him. But it so happened that at that moment the whole professoriate was absorbed in one of those great educational crises which from time to time shake a university to its base. The meeting of the faculty that day bid fair to lose all vestige of decorum in the excitement of the moment. For, as Dean Elderberry Foible, the head of the faculty, said, the motion that they had before them amounted practically to a revolution. The proposal was nothing less than the permission of the use of lead-pencils instead of pen and ink in the sessional examinations of the university. Anyone conversant with the inner life of a college will realise that to many of the professoriate this was nothing less than a last wild onslaught of socialistic democracy against the solid bulwarks of society. They must fight it back or die on the walls. To others it was one more step in the splendid progress of democratic education, comparable only to such epoch-making things as the abandonment of the cap and gown, and the omission of the word "sir" in speaking to a professor.

No wonder that the fight raged. Elderberry Foible, his fluffed white hair almost on end, beat in vain with his gavel for order. Finally, Chang of Physiology, who was a perfect dynamo of energy and was known frequently to work for three or four hours at a stretch, proposed that the faculty should adjourn the question and meet for its further discussion on the following Saturday morning. This revolutionary suggestion, involving work on Saturday, reduced the meeting to a mere turmoil, in the midst of which Elderberry Foible proposed that the whole question of the use of lead-pencils should be adjourned till that day six months, and that meantime a new special committee of seventeen professors, with power to add to their number, to call witnesses and, if need be, to hear them, should report on the entire matter *de novo*.   This motion, after the striking out of the words *de novo* and the insertion of *ab initio*, was finally carried, after which the faculty sank back completely exhausted into its chair, the need of afternoon tea and toast stamped on every face.

And it was at this moment that President Boomer, who understood faculties as few men have done, quietly entered the room, laid his silk hat on a volume of Demosthenes, and proposed the vote of a degree of Doctor of Letters for Edward Tomlinson.   He said that there was no need to remind the faculty of Tomlinson's services to the nation; they knew them.   Of the members of the faculty, indeed, some thought that he meant the Tomlinson who wrote the famous monologue on the Iota Subscript, while others supposed that he referred to the celebrated philosopher Tomlinson, whose new book on the Indivisibility of the Inseparable was just then maddening the entire world.   In any case, they voted the degree without a word, still faint with exhaustion.

.     .     .     .     .     .     .

But while the university was conferring on Tomlinson the degree of Doctor of Letters, all over the City in business circles they were conferring on him far other titles. "Idiot," "Scoundrel," "Swindler," were the least of them. Every stock and share with which his name was known to be connected was coming down with a run, wiping out the accumulated profits of the Wizard at the rate of a thousand dollars a minute.

They not only questioned his honesty, but they went further and questioned his business capacity.

"The man," said Mr. Lucullus Fyshe, sitting in the Mausoleum Club and breathing freely at last after having disposed of all his holdings in the Erie Auriferous, "is an ignoramus. I asked him only the only day, quite casually, a perfectly simple business question. I said to him, 'T. C. Bonds have risen twenty-two and a half in a week. You know and I know that they are only collateral trust, and that the stock underneath never could and never would earn a par dividend. Now,' I said, for I wanted to test the fellow, 'tell me what that means?' Would you believe me, he looked me right in the face in that stupid way of his, and he said, 'I don't know!' "

"He said he didn't know!" repeated the listener contemptuously; "the man is a damn fool!"

.    .    .    .    .    .    .

The reason of all this was that the results of the researches of the professor of geology were being whispered among the directorate of the Erie Auriferous. And the directors and chief shareholders were busily performing the interesting process called unloading. Nor did ever a farmer of Cahoga County in haying time, with a thunderstorm threatening, unload with greater rapidity than did the major shareholders of the Auriferous. Mr. Lucullus Fyshe traded off a quarter of his stock to an unwary member of the Mausoleum Club at a drop of thirty per cent., and being too prudent to hold the rest on any terms he conveyed it at once as a benefaction in trust to the Plutorian Orphans' and Foundlings' Home; while the purchaser of Mr. Fyshe's stock, learning too late of his folly, rushed for his lawyers to have the shares conveyed as a gift to the Home for Incurables.

Mr. Asmodeus Boulder transferred his entire holdings to the Imbeciles' Relief Society, and Mr. Furlong, senior, passed his over to a Chinese mission as fast as pen could traverse paper.

Down at the office of Skinyer and Beatem, the lawyers of the company, they were working overtime drawing up deeds and conveyances and trusts in perpetuity, with hardly time to put them into typewriting. Within twenty-four hours the entire stock of the company bid fair to be in the hands of Idiots, Orphans, Protestants, Foundlings, Imbeciles, Missionaries, Chinese, and other unfinancial people, with Tomlinson the Wizard of Finance as the senior shareholder and majority control. And whether the gentle Wizard, as he sat with mother planning his vast benefaction to Plutoria University, would have felt more at home with his new group of fellow-shareholders than his old, it were hard indeed to say.

But meantime at the office of Skinyer and Beatem all was activity. For not only were they drafting the conveyances of the perpetual trusts as fast as legal brains working overtime could do it, but in another part of the office a section of the firm were busily making their preparations against the expected actions for fraud and warrants of distraint and injunctions against disposal of assets and the whole battery of artillery which might open on them at any moment. And they worked like a corps of military engineers fortifying an escarpment, with the joy of battle in their faces.

The storm might break at any moment. Already at the office of the *Financial Undertone* the type was set for a special extra with a heading three inches high:

## COLLAPSE
## OF THE ERIE CONSOLIDATED

### ARREST OF THE MAN TOMLINSON
### EXPECTED THIS AFTERNOON

Skinyer and Beatem had paid the editor, who was crooked, two thousand dollars cash to hold back that extra for twenty-four hours; and the editor had paid the reporting staff, who were crooked, twenty-five dollars each to keep the news quiet, and the compositors, who were also crooked, ten dollars per man to hold their mouths shut till the morning, with the result that from editors and sub-editors and reporters and compositors the news went seething forth in a flood that the Erie Auriferous Consolidated was going to shatter into fragments like the bursting of a dynamite bomb. It rushed with a thousand whispering tongues from street to street, till it filled the corridors of the law-courts and the lobbies of the offices, and till every honest man that held a share of the stock shivered in his tracks and reached out to give, sell, or destroy it. Only the unwinking Idiots, and the mild Orphans, and the calm Deaf-mutes, and the impassive Chinese held tight to what they had. So gathered the storm, till all the town, like the great rotunda of the Grand Palaver, was filled with a silent "call for Mr. Tomlinson," voiceless and ominous.

And while all this was happening, and while at Skinyer and Beatem's they worked with frantic pens and clattering type, there came a knock at the door, hesitant and uncertain, and before the eyes of the astounded office there stood in his wide-awake hat and long black coat the figure of "the man Tomlinson" himself.

And Skinyer, the senior partner, no sooner heard what Tomlinson wanted than he dashed across the outer office to his partner's room with his hyena face all excitement as he said:

"Beatem, Beatem, come over to my room. This man is absolutely the biggest thing in America. For sheer calmness and nerve I never heard of anything to approach him. What do you think he wants to do?"

"What?" said Beatem.

"Why, he's giving his entire fortune to the university."

"By Gad!" ejaculated Beatem, and the two lawyers looked at one another, lost in admiration of the marvellous genius and assurance of Tomlinson.

. . . . . . .

Yet what had happened was very simple.

Tomlinson had come back from the university filled with mingled hope and hesitation. The university, he saw, needed the money, and he hoped to give it his entire fortune, to put Dr. Boomer in a position to practically destroy the whole place. But, like many a modest man, he lacked the assurance to speak out. He felt that up to the present the benefactors of the university had been men of an entirely different class from himself.

It was mother who solved the situation for him.

"Well, father," she said, "there's one thing I've learned already since we've had money. If you want to get a thing done you can always find people to do it for you if you pay them. Why not go to those lawyers that manage things for the company and get them to arrange it all for you with the college?"

As a result, Tomlinson had turned up at the door of the Skinyer and Beatem office.

. . . . . . .

"Quite so, Mr. Tomlinson," said Skinyer, with his pen already dipped in the ink, "a perfectly simple matter. I can draw up a draft of conveyance with a few strokes of the pen. In fact, we can do it on the spot."

What he meant was, "In fact, we can do it so fast that I can pocket a fee of five hundred dollars right here and now while you have the money to pay me."

"Yes, and it's a good thing I didn't lose the money when I tried to. You see, mother, what I hadn't realised was the good that could be done with all that money if a man put his heart into it. They can start in as soon as they like and tear down those buildings. My! but it's just wonderful what you can do with money. I'm glad I didn't lose it."

So they talked far into the evening. That night they slept in an Aladdin's palace filled with golden fancies.

And in the morning the palace and all its visions fell tumbling about their heads in sudden and awful catastrophe. For with Tomlinson's first descent to the rotunda it broke. The whole great space seemed filled with the bulletins and the broadside sheets of the morning papers, the crowd surging to and fro buying the papers, men reading them as they stood, and everywhere in great letters there met his eye:

COLLAPSE
OF THE ERIE AURIFEROUS

THE GREAT GOLD SWINDLE

ARREST OF THE MAN TOMLINSON
EXPECTED THIS MORNING

So stood the Wizard of Finance beside a pillar, the paper fluttering in his hand, his eyes fixed, while about him a thousand eager eyes and rushing tongues sent shame into his stricken heart.

And there his boy Fred, sent from upstairs, found him; and at the sight of the seething crowd and his father's stricken face, aged as it seemed all in a moment, the boy's soul woke within him. What had happened he could not tell, only that his father stood there, dazed, beaten, and staring at him on every side in giant letters:

## ARREST OF THE MAN TOMLINSON

"Come, father, come upstairs," he said, and took him by the arm, dragging him through the crowd.

In the next half-hour as they sat and waited for the arrest in the false grandeur of the thousand-dollar suite,— Tomlinson, his wife, and Fred,—the boy learnt more than all the teaching of the industrial faculty of Plutoria University could have taught him in a decade.  Adversity laid its hand upon him, and at its touch his adolescent heart turned to finer stuff than the salted gold of the Erie Auriferous.  As he looked upon his father's broken figure waiting meekly for arrest, and his mother's blubbered face, a great wrath burned itself into his soul.

"When the sheriff comes—" said Tomlinson, and his lip trembled as he spoke.  He had no other picture of arrest than that.

"They can't arrest you, father," broke out the boy. "You've done nothing.  You never swindled them.  I tell you, if they try to arrest you, I'll—" and his voice broke and stopped upon a sob, and his hands clenched in passion.

"You stay here, you and mother.  I'll go down.  Give me your money and I'll go and pay them and we'll get out of this and go home.  They can't stop us; there's nothing to arrest you for."

Nor was there.  Fred paid the bill unmolested, save for the prying eyes and babbling tongues of the rotunda.

And a few hours from that, while the town was still ringing with news of his downfall, the Wizard with his wife and son walked down from their thousand-dollar suite into the corridor, their hands burdened with their satchels.  A waiter, with something between a sneer and an obsequious smile upon his face, reached out for the valises, wondering if it was still worth while.

"You get to hell out of that!" said Fred.  He had put on again his rough store suit in which he had come from Cahoga County, and there was a dangerous look about his big shoulders and his set jaw.  And the waiter slunk back.

So did they pass, unarrested and unhindered, through corridor and rotunda to the outer portals of the great hotel.

Beside the door of the Palaver as they passed out was a tall official with a uniform and a round hat.  He was called by the authorities a *chasseur* or a *commissionaire*, or some foreign name to mean that he did nothing.

At the sight of him the Wizard's face flushed for a moment, with a look of his old perplexity.

"I wonder," he began to murmur, "how much I ought—"

"Not a damn cent, father," said Fred, as he shouldered past the magnificent *chasseur*; "let him work."

With which admirable doctrine the Wizard and his son passed from the portals of the Grand Palaver.

.      .      .      .      .      .      .

Nor was there any arrest either then or later.  In spite of the expectations of the rotunda and the announcements of the *Financial Undertone*, the "man Tomlinson" was *not* arrested, neither as he left the Grand Palaver nor as he stood waiting at the railroad station with Fred and mother for the outgoing train for Cahoga County.

There was nothing to arrest him for.  That was not the least strange part of the career of the Wizard of Finance.  For when all the affairs of the Erie Auriferous Consolidated were presently calculated up by the labours of Skinyer and Beatem and the legal representatives of the Orphans and the Idiots and the Deaf-mutes, they resolved themselves into the most beautiful and complete cipher conceivable.  The salted gold about paid for the cost of the incorporation certificate: the development capital had disappeared, and those who lost most preferred to say the least about it; and as for Tomlinson, if one added up his gains on the stock market before the fall and subtracted his bill at the Grand Palaver and the thousand dollars which he gave to Skinyer and Beatem to recover his freehold on the lower half of his farm, and the cost of three tickets to Cahoga station, the debit and credit account balanced to a hair.

Thus did the whole fortune of Tomlinson vanish in a night, even as the golden palace seen in the mirage of a desert sunset may fade before the eyes of the beholder, and leave no trace behind.

.    .    .    .    .    .    .

It was some months after the collapse of the Erie Auriferous that the university conferred upon Tomlinson the degree of Doctor of Letters *in absentia*.  A university must keep its word, and Dean Elderberry Foible, who was honesty itself, had stubbornly maintained that a vote of the faculty of arts once taken and written in the minute book became as irrefragable as the Devonian rock itself.

So the degree was conferred.  And Dean Elderberry Foible, standing in a long red gown before Dr. Boomer, seated in a long blue gown, read out after the ancient custom of the college the Latin statement of the award of the degree of Doctor of Letters, "Eduardus Tomlinsonius, vir clarissimus, doctissimus, præstissimus," and a great many other things all ending in *issimus*.

But the recipient was not there to receive.  He stood

at that moment with his boy Fred on a windy hill-side beside Lake Erie, where Tomlinson's Creek ran again untrammelled to the lake.  Nor was the scene altered to the eye, for Tomlinson and his son had long since broken a hole in the dam with pickaxe and crowbar, and day by day the angry water carried down the vestiges of the embankment till all were gone.  The cedar poles of the electric lights had been cut into fence-rails; the wooden shanties of the Italian gang of Auriferous workers had been torn down and split into firewood; and where they had stood, the burdocks and the thistles of the luxuriant summer conspired to hide the traces of their shame.  Nature reached out its hand and drew its coverlet of green over the grave of the vanished Eldorado.

And as the Wizard and his son stood upon the hill-side, they saw nothing but the land sloping to the lake and the creek murmuring again to the willows, while the off-shore wind rippled the rushes of the shallow water.

# On the Need for a Quiet College

IF somebody would give me about two dozen very old elm trees and about fifty acres of wooded ground and lawn—not too near anywhere and not too far from everywhere—I think I could set up a college that would put all the big universities of today in the shade. I am not saying that it would be better. But it would be different.

I would need a few buildings, but it doesn't take many —stone, if possible—and a belfry and a clock. The clock wouldn't need to go; it might be better if it didn't. I would want some books—a few thousand would do—and some apparatus. But it's amazing how little apparatus is needed for scientific work of the highest quality: in fact "the higher the fewer."

Most of all, I should need a set of professors. I would need only a dozen of them—but they'd have to be real ones —disinterested men of learning, who didn't even know they were distinterested. And, mind you, these professors of mine wouldn't sit in "offices" dictating letters on "cases" to stenographers, and only leaving their offices to go to "committees" and "conferences." There would be no "offices" in my college and no "committees," and my professors would have no time for conferences, because the job they would be on would need all eternity and would never be finished.

My professors would never be findable at any fixed place except when they were actually giving lectures. Men of thought have no business in an office. Learning runs away from "committee." There would be no "check up" on the time of the professors: there would be no "hire and fire" or "judge by results" or "standards" or "norms" of work for them: or any fixed number of hours.

But, on the other hand, they would, if I got the ones I want, be well worth their apparent irresponsibility: and when they lectured each one would be, though he wouldn't know it, a magician—with such an interest and absorption that those who listened would catch the infection of it, and hurry from the lecture to the library, still warm with thought.

It must be understood that the work of professors is peculiar. Few professors, real ones, ever complete their work: what they give to the world is fragments. The rest remains. Their contributions must be added up, not measured singly. Every professor has his "life work" and sometimes does it, and sometimes dies first.

I can recall—I say it by way of digression—one such who was working on Machiavelli. When I first met him he had worked fourteen years. He worked in a large room covered a foot deep with Machiavelli—notes, pamphlets, remains. I asked him—it seemed a simple question—what he thought of Machiavelli. He shook his head. He said it was too soon to form an opinion. Later, ten years later, he published his book, *Machiavelli*. One of the great continental reviews—one of the really great ones (you and I never hear of them: they have a circulation of about 300) said his work was based on premature judgments. He was hurt, but he felt it was true. He had rushed into print too soon.

Another such devoted himself—he began years ago—to the history of the tariff. He began in a quiet lull of tariff changes when for three or four years public attention was elsewhere. He brought his work up to within a year or so of actual up-to-date completeness. Then the tariff began to move: two years later he was three years behind it.

Presently, though he worked hard, he was five years behind it.

He has never caught it. His only hope now is that the tariff will move back towards free trade, and meet him.

Not that I mean to imply that my professors would be a pack of nuts or freaks. Not at all: their manners might be dreamy and their clothes untidy but they'd be—they'd have to be—the most eminent men in their subjects. To get them would be the main effort of the college: to coax them, buy them, if need be, to kidnap them. Nothing counts beside that. A college is made of men, not by the size of buildings, number of students and football records. But trustees don't know this, or, at best, catch only a glimmer of it and lose it. Within a generation all the greatest books on the humanities would come from my college.

The professors bring the students. The students bring, unsought, the benefactions. The thing feeds itself like a flame in straw. But it's the men that count. A college doesn't need students: it's the students who need the college.

After twenty years my college would stand all alone. There are little colleges now but they ape bigness. There are quiet colleges but they try to be noisy. There are colleges without big games but they boom little ones. Mine would seem the only one, because the chance is there, wide open, and no one takes it. After twenty years people would drive in motor cars to see my college: and wouldn't be let in.

Round such a college there must be no thought of money. Money ruins life: I mean, to have to think of it, to take account of it, to know that it is there. Men apart from money, men in an army, men on an expedition of exploration, emerge to a new life. Money is gone. At times and places whole classes thus lift up, or partly: as in older countries like England the class called "gentry" that once was. These people lived on land and money from the past—stolen, perhaps, five hundred years ago—and so thought no more of it. They couldn't earn more; they didn't know how. They kept what they had, or dropped out, fell through a trestle bridge of social structure and were gone in the stream. This class, in America, we never had. They grow rare everywhere. Perhaps we don't want them. But they had the good luck that, in their lives, money in the sense here meant, didn't enter. Certain money limits circumscribed their life, but from day to day they never thought of it. A cow in a pasture, a fairly generous pasture, doesn't know it's in. It thinks it's outside. So did they.

So I would have it in my college. Students not rich and not poor—or not using their wealth and not feeling their poverty—an equality as unconscious as that where Evangeline lived.

Nor would their studies lead to, or aim at, or connect with wealth. The so-called practical studies are all astray. Real study, real learning must, for the individual, be quite valueless or it loses its value. The proper studies for my college are history and literature and philosophy and thought and poetry and speculation, in the pursuit of which each shall repeat the eager search, the unending quest, of the past. Looking for one thing he shall find another. Looking for ultimate truth, which is unfindable, they will learn at least to repudiate all that is false.

I leave out at one sweep great masses of stuff usually taught: all that goes under such a name as a university faculty of Commerce. There is no such thing. The faculty of Commerce is down at the docks, at Wall Street, in the steel mills.  A "degree" in Commerce is a salary of ten thousand a year.  Those who fail to pass go to Atlanta —and stay there.  Certain things in Commerce are teachable: accountancy, corporate organization and the principles of embezzlement.  But that's not a university.

Out goes economics, except as speculation: not a thing to teach in instalments and propositions like geometry. You *can't* teach it.  No one knows it.  It's the riddle of the Sphinx.  My graduates will be just nicely fitted to think about it when they come out.  A first-year girl studying economics is as wide of the mark as an old man studying cosmetics.  The philosophical speculative analysis of our economic life is the highest study of all, next to the riddle of our existence.  But to cut it into classes and credits is a parody.  Out it goes.

Out—but to come back again—goes medicine.  Medicine is a great reality: it belongs in a *school,* not a college. My college fits people to study medicine, study it in crowded cities among gas-lights and ambulances and hospitals and human suffering, and keep their souls alive while they do it.  Then later, as trained men in the noblest profession in the world, the atmosphere of the college, which they imbibed among my elm trees, grows about them again.  The last word in cultivation is, and always has been, the cultivated "medicine man."

The engineers?—that's different.  Theirs is the most "manly" of all the professions—among water power and gold mines and throwing bridges half a mile at a throw. But it's a *school* that trains them, not a college.  They go to my college but they don't like it.  They say it's too damn dreamy.  So they kick out of it into engineering. For a time they remember the Latin third declension. Presently they forget it.  Doctors grow cultivated as they grow older.  Engineers get rougher and rougher.

What I mean is that our studies have drifted away, away from the single-minded absorption of learning. Our students of today live in a whirl and clatter of "student activities." They have, in any large college, at least a hundred organizations and societies. They are "all up!" for this today and "all out!" for that tomorrow. Life is a continuous rally! a rah, rah! a parade! They play no games: they use teams for that. But exercise, and air, is their life. They *root,* in an organized hysteria, a code of signals telling them what to feel. They root, they rush, they organize, they play politics, run newspapers—and when they step from college into life, they fit it absolutely, having lived already.

No one is denying here what fine men and women college makes, physically fine and mentally alert. Any one of them could run an elevator the day he steps out of college.

But there's something wanting: do they *think?* Or is there anything after all to think about? And yet, surely, in the long run the world has lived on its speculative minds. Or hasn't it?

Some who think of course there must be. You can't submerge humanity in two generations. But mostly, I believe, the little poets fade out on their first-year benches, and the wistful intelligence learns to say *"Rah! Rah!"* and is lost.

Not so in my college. There will be no newspaper, except a last week's paper from the back counties of New England. There will be no politics because there will be no offices to run for. My students will control nothing. The whole movement of student control is a mistake. They're so busy controlling that they're not students.

They shall play games all they want to, but as games, not as a profession, not as college advertising—and no gate receipts. Till only a few years ago the country that taught the world its games, played them as apart from money—as far apart as sheer necessity allowed. If Waterloo was won on the playing fields of Eton (it wasn't, really: it was won in Belgium), there was at least no stadium at two dollars a seat.

One asks, perhaps, about the endowments, about the benefactors of my ideal college. The benefactors are all dead: or at least they must act as if they were. Years ago on the prairies many authorities claimed that the only good Indian was a dead Indian. It may not have been true. But it is certainly true that the best college benefactor is a dead one. After all, the reward in the long run is his, those sculptured letters graven in the stone, "To the greater glory of God and in memory of Johannes Smith." That, in a college among elm trees—that's worth a lifetime of gifts, given and given gladly. Such things should best be graven in Latin. In my college they will be; Latin and lots of it, all over the place, with the mystic conspiracy of pretence, the wholesome humbug, that those who see it know what it means. Latin lasts. English seems to alter every thousand years or so. It's like the tariff that I named above—too mobile for academic use.

As with the benefactors, so with the managing trustees who look after the money and never lose it. Not dead, these, but very silent: solid men who don't need to talk and don't, but who can invest a million dollars over three depressions, and there it still is, like gold in a pot in the Pyramids. You find them chiefly in New England, at least I seem to have seen them there, more than anywhere else. They are at the head of huge investment businesses, so big that you never hear of them. Mostly, if they don't talk, it means that they are thinking where to place fifty million dollars. You see, they hate to break it.

And women? The arrangements in my college for the women students, and the women's dormitories? Oh, no—no, thank you. There aren't any women. Coeducation is a wonderful thing for women: college girls under coeducation leave college more fit to leave college than any others. College girls are better companions, better wives (as your own or as someone else's) than any others. It's the women who have made our college life the bright, happy thing it is—too bright, too happy.

But men can't *study* when women are around. And it's not only the students. If I let the women in, they'd get round some of my dusty old professors, and marry them—and good-bye to Machiavelli, and the higher thought.

# Turn Back the Clock

*Or, at Least, Make It Slower*

ALL of us who are old look back with a sort of wistful admiration to the education that we received long ago—so different from the education of today. I remember many years ago, when I was a junior professor at McGill University, meeting an elderly Scottish divine who questioned me about the nature of our curriculum. He was horrified to find that the students were actually allowed a certain amount of choice, or election, in making up the programme of their studies. "When I was at Edinburgh," he said, shaking his head, "the whole of the studies were absolutely compulsory." With that he shuffled off, smacking his lips over the word *compulsory,* and musing, no doubt, on the degeneracy of the time.

A similar point of view, as I have mentioned in another connection, was expressed once in a discussion at my club about education, involving the topic of the classics. A scholarly English visitor to the Club, a Bishop, said very emphatically—"Well, all I can say is that I regard Greek as having practically made me what I am." There was a silence, and then an American present said, "Exactly!" But the Bishop didn't see it—one of the advantages, no doubt, of learning Greek.

Such views of our own past education belong, I do not doubt, to the illusions of retrospect. They have all the soft colour and mellow tints that surround the "good old times," and the "old school" and reach away back to the distant past of "Merrie England" and the "brave days of

299

old." The pain and distress dies out of our human record as we look back on it.

But even if we grant that modern education has in the main meant progress, we may still note many things of value that have somehow been dropped by the way—and the faster the pace of progress the larger the likelihood of such losses. One grants, I said, the progress, the improvement. The "little red school house" of sixty years ago, taken as a reality, looks but a poor structure, ill-lighted and unventilated, beside the "academy" of today—its windows all to the sun, its rooms as neat and bright as day, its wide corridors decorated with the framed pictures of great men. In it is its teacher, as highly certified and as guaranteed as a patent pump, and at his command a whole battery of instruction by radio and screen, and loud speaker, with apparatus to illustrate everything so clearly as to obviate all thought.

More than that. The new teacher is very different from the old "dominie" and the bye-gone "schoolmarm," in that he is a "pedagogue" with a pedagogical certificate to prove it. He knows the principles of education, whereas sixty years ago none of us dreamed that there were any. He knows that education must proceed from the known to the unknown and from the concrete to the abstract. He knows, or he thinks he knows, that learning things is of no value unless you clearly understand what they mean: otherwise your knowledge is just that of a parrot. He does not realize that the Bishop and I—I mean the bishop of whom I just spoke—having been very largely trained as "parrots" along with a whole generation of other young parrots, would regret very much to admit that there is absolutely nothing in the bird at all.

The field that is suggested is so wide—this problem as to what our rational education may have lost in becoming so

—that one can do no more than skirt its outline, or indicate one or two of the eminences or depressions of its landscape that seem of peculiar significance. Here is one broad feature of the prospect—the element of hardship, of compulsion, of disagreeableness. Modern education has set itself to make its processes attractive, to substitute the element of spontaneous interest for the element of compulsion by force. Learning at the point of a stick, corporal punishment, and learning under the threat of detention—the school-world equivalent of the gallows and the jail—are out of fashion now. It is the idea of our education that learning must be free and happy, carrying its own interest, and at least relying more on rewards than on punishments. Seen thus the interest of each bright little school building becomes for the child a vision of what the world might be, could we so order it; and above all, for the children of poverty, some little taste of the warmth and amenity of life.

These tendencies and these ideas must in the main be true. I may say, indeed, that I am sure they are, for I can look back over sixty-four years of school and college class rooms and I have seen the change. I recall that when I first went to school in England, as a child of four, there had newly come into use a little text called *Reading Without Tears*. Observe the revolutionary title. Older people shook their heads at it. Till then, the tears that fell upon the page, softened it to its value. The Beth-el of education was built of the stone blocks of hardship. The steeper the road to Parnassus the more was the body fortified in climbing it.

We are at too great pains now to make our education easy, at too great pains to avoid sustained hardship. We prefer to give to the children the pretty little mechanical fancies that belong to the nursery in place of tears. Our text books multiply the devices of ease—the little résumé that replaces the ensemble, the quick and easy "selection" that reduces a poem to a verse and a stanza to a line; the total omission of factors that seem "too difficult," such as the "quantities" of Latin words. In place of Plato, students study a "Plato-made-easy"—by ceasing to be Plato. I know of a great university—I won't name it; it begins with an M—which gave up First Year Physics as a compulsory subject because "the girls couldn't learn it."

Every foot of this ground, of course, is uncertain with doubt, and undermined with controversy. But I incline to think that we overdo now the elements that were of such high value when they came as over-needed innovations. The point is that our new mechanical environment —radio, motion pictures, the voices in the air and the figures on the screen—make presentation so direct, so easy, so physical that they tend to put the human imagination to sleep. The sheer rapidity of them precludes depth; the multiplicity of them defies memory. There are no "indelible impressions" left.

To the child of fifty years ago the world of books was one of intense imaginative creations—the work of its own responsive mind. What child could forget its conjured vision of Robinson Crusoe bending over the yellow sand that bore the imprint of Friday's foot! What reader of Tom Sawyer could forget the gloomy horror of the great cave—with Indian Joe walled up in it—the great cave of which he himself—his own imagination—was, under Mark Twain's guidance—the sole architect. All of our pictured world was ours. But compare with it the typical modern child of the cities, lolling at his movies, saturated and unsurprisable, impervious, after the age of about ten, to further impressions of scenery, an expert in murder, a cynic on women—for whom all the world's masterpieces have been done over into flickered sensationalism.

What such a child needs when he goes to school is not the primrose path of ease, the escalator to Parnassus, but a touch of the good old hard stuff such as the Bishop and I got, and the Edinburgh divine.  If he doesn't, there will soon be no more men left like us, and that would be too bad.

# First Call for Spring

—*or*—

## *Oh, Listen to the Birds*

I GATHER that spring is approaching. I am not an observant man, but as the days go by, the signs begin to multiply. Even for me that means that spring is at hand.

I take this early occasion to notify the public of my opinion and to support it with collateral facts. I am anxious this year to be among the first in the field. Among the signs on which I base my views that spring is near, I may mention that I observe that the snow has gone: that the income tax declarations are being distributed at the post-office; and that the sign BOCK BEER is hung out.

Spring then is upon us. The first call for spring has come: and I should like to suggest that this year we meet it firmly and quietly and with none of the hysterical outburst that it usually provokes in people of a certain temperament. I refer to those unfortunate beings called "lovers of nature."

Each year I have been pained to notice that the approach of spring occasions a most distressing aberration in the conduct of many of my friends. Beside my house, a few doors on the right, I have an acquaintance who is a Nature Man. All through the winter he is fairly quiet, and an agreeable friendly fellow, quite fit for general society. I notice him, it is true, occasionally grubbing under the snow. I have once or twice seen him break off a frozen twig from a tree, and examine it. On one occasion, indeed, last winter he was temporarily unmanned by seeing a black bird (otherwise harmless) sitting on a bough. But for the most part his conduct during the colder weather is entirely normal.

Spring, however, at once occasions in my Nature friend a distressing disturbance. He seems suddenly to desire, at our every meeting, to make himself a channel of information as between the animate world and me. From the moment that the snow begins to melt, he keeps me posted as to what the plants and the birds and the bees are doing. This is a class of information which I do not want, and which I cannot use. But I have to bear it.

My Nature friend passes me every morning with some new and bright piece of information: something that he thinks so cheery that irradiates his face. "I saw a finch this morning," he says. "Oh, did you," I answer. "I noticed a scarlet tanager this afternoon," says my friend. "You don't say so!" I reply. What a tanager is I have never known: I hope I never shall. When my Nature friend says things of this sort all I can do is to acquiesce. I can't match his information in any way. In point of ornithology I only know two birds, the crow and the hen. I can tell them at once either by their plumage or by their song. I can carry on a nature conversation up to the limit of the crow and the hen; beyond that, not.

So for the first day or so in spring, I am able to say, "I saw a crow yesterday," or "I noticed a hen out walking this morning." But somehow my crow and hen seem to get out of date awfully quickly. I get ashamed of them and never refer to them again. But my friend keeps up his information for weeks, running through a whole gamut of animals. "I saw a gopher the other day," he says, "guess what the little fellow was doing?" If only he knew it I'd like to break out and answer, "I don't care what the Hades the little fellow was doing." But, like everybody else, I suppose, I have not the assurance or the cruelty to break in upon the rapture of the Nature Man. Some day I shall: and when I do, let him watch out.

My particular anger with these Nature Men such as my friend, springs, I think, from the singularly irritating kind of language that they use: a sort of ingratiating wee-wee way in which they amalgamate themselves, as it were, with Nature. They really seem to feel so cute about it. If a wee hepatica peeps above the snow they think they've done it. They describe it to you in a peculiar line of talk almost like baby language. "What do you think I saw?" says the Nature Man. "Just the tiniest little shoot of green peeping from the red-brown of the willow!" He imitates it with his thumb and finger to show the way the tiny little shoot shoots. I suppose he thinks he's a little bud himself. I really believe that my particular friend actually imagines himself in spring-time to be a wee hepatica, or a first crocus, or the yellow-underleaf of a daffodil.

And notice, too, the way in which they refer to colours; never plain and simple ones like red or black or blue; always stuff like "red-brown" or "blue-green." My friend asks me if I have noticed the peculiar soft "yellow-brown" that the water fowl puts on in spring. Answer: No, I haven't: I haven't seen any water-fowl: I don't know where you look for them and I didn't know that they put anything on. As for "yellow-brown" I didn't know that there was any such colour. I have seen a blue-black crow this year, and I have noticed a burnt-indigo-sepia hen: but beyond that I have not seen anything doing.

Worst of all, and, in fact, verging on paresis is the state of mind of the Nature Man in regard to the birds. When he speaks of them his voice takes on a peculiar whine. My Nature friend told me yesterday that he had seen two orioles just beginning to build a nest behind his garage. He said he "tiptoed" to the spot (notice the peculiar wee-wee language that these people use)—and then stood rooted there watching them. I forget whether he said "rooted" or "riveted": on occasions like this he sometimes reports himself as one and sometimes as the other. But why on earth, if he is once fairly rooted, does he come unrooted again?

I therefore wish to give this plain and simple notice, meant without malice: If any other of my friends has noticed a snowdrop just peeping above the edge of the turf, will he mind not telling me. If any of them has noticed that the inner bark of the oak is beginning to blush a faint blue-red, would he mind keeping it to himself. If there is any man that I know who has seen two orioles starting to build a nest behind his garage, and if he has stood rooted to the ground with interest and watched the dear little feathered pair fluttering to and fro, would he object to staying rooted and saying nothing about it?

I am aware that I ought long ago to have spoken out openly to my Nature friends. But I have, I admit, the unfortunate and weak-minded disposition that forces me to smile with hatred in my heart. My unhappy neighbour does not suspect that I mean to kill him. But I do. I have stood for all that tanager and oriole stuff that I can. The end is coming. And as for that hepatica just putting its tiny face above the brown of the leaf—well, wait, that's all. Some day, I know it, I shall all of a sudden draw a revolver on my friend and say, "Listen. This has gone far enough. Every spring for many years you have stopped me in the street and told me of this Nature stuff. And I have stood for it and smiled. You told me when the first touch of brown appeared on the underwing of the lark, and I let you say it. You kept me posted as to when the first trillium appeared from a pile of dead oak leaves under a brush-heap: and I let you tell it to me and never said that all I knew of trilliums was in connection with the German reparations indemnity. But the thing is exhausted. Meet your fate as you can. You are going where the first purple-pink of the young rhododendron will be of no interest to you."

I don't want to appear surly. But I am free to admit that I am the kind of man who would never notice an oriole building a nest unless it came and built it in my hat in the hat room of the club. There are other men like me too: and the time has come when we must protect ourselves. There are signs of spring that every sensible man respects and recognizes. He sees the oyster disappear from the club bill-of-fare, and knows that winter is passing; he watches boiled new California potatoes fall from 25 to 10 cents a portion and realizes that the season is advancing. He notes the first timid appearance of the asparagus just peeping out of its melted butter: and he sees the first soft blush on the edge of the Carolina Strawberry at one-dollar-and-fifty cents a box. And he watches, or he used to watch, in the old day beyond recall, for the sign BOCK BEER TO-DAY that told him that all nature was glad.

These are the signs of spring that any man can appreciate. They speak for themselves. Viewed thus, I am as sensitive to the first call for spring as any of my fellows. I like to sit in my club with my fellow members of like mind and watch its coming and herald its approach.

But for the kind of spring that needs a whole text book of biology to interpret it, I have neither use nor sympathy.

# Hand Me Down that Book

IT is an old dispute whether fancy is greater than fact, fiction superior to reality, and the creation of the imagination more significant than the literal truth of the intellect. To put it more simply—which do you find more real—Mr. Pickwick whom you know from the garters up and from the heart out, or Mr. Jones, next door? Night after night you've talked with Mr. Jones while he sprinkled his lawn with a hose. He has expressed his opinion on the extent which grass can be kept green all summer and he has agreed with you that after all the city in the summer is the best summer resort that there is. But apart from that, do you *know* him? No, practically not. Would he lend you money? Oh! no! Would Mr. Pickwick? My dear sir, you'd only have to ask. He'd send it over by Sam Weller within ten minutes with a warning that there must be no thought of repayment.

That's what "people in books" are like—real people to whom your heart responds and who mean more to you than the people of your everyday life. Many of them have come down with you from your childhood. With some of them you have faced danger on the sea, when one more crack in the top-gallant-mast might mean instant disaster; or in the pathless woods of North America, where the careless cracking of a dry twig under the foot of either of you could have brought an arrow whizzing past your head. It wouldn't have hit you, of course. In the glorious world of books, arrows never *hit* you, they just "whizz past"; and bullets "sing"; or even "rattle" when thick enough—but you come out of it all right, always. Another contrast, this, with real life, whose poor disasters are so mean, so desolating, so shabby and so unrelieved.

What a cavalcade they form, these "people out of books" as they come from away back down the centuries. Some are in the very dawn of history, the mist still all about them. Here is Hector with his tall helmet, and Achilles who dragged him around the walls of Troy—or, wait a bit, was it Achilles who dragged Hector, or was it Hector who dragged Achilles?—And, let me think, were they dragged, or *drugged?*—I'm afraid I'm mixing it up with that latest movie; did you see it? I can't quite remember the name—anyway, the one where the Chinaman, Hong Something, drugs the detective—at least he *thinks* he's a detective.

The trouble is, of course, that in these later days—nobody's fault—the old outlines are getting dim—all sorts of other and newer and quicker impressions are being written over them. The flash of the cinematograph fuses our history like a burnt-out wire, till the pictures melt and run and mix and somehow reform to make a kaleidoscope of moving mice, of flying rabbits, of dancing scenery, of rushing trains, fleeing criminals, detectives . . . and throughout all, today's news, crashing with bombs, louder than the ten years' siege of Troy, and forgotten in a week.

Those of us old enough can still look through this foreground of the moment to the cavalcade of giants, heroes, warriors, knights, and ladies that gradually made the literature of the world. We can still hear the laughter of Chaucer's Pilgrims of Canterbury, easy and sauntering, with always time for a joke, the worse the better—how different from the hurrying tourist of today with his radio in his ear as he sleeps. We can still wander with Don Quixote, driving full speed at windmills, with the haunting feeling that there's a double meaning in it all if we could only catch it. Or here, closer at hand is Falstaff— it's a pity the young people of today don't know him; they'd find him "some boy." Or here is *Sir Roger de Coverley*—never read it? Oh, you must—and the *Vicar of Wakefield*—and then round the corner into the full noonday sun of the nineteenth century, with its whole procession of *Waverleys* and *Ivanhoes,* its Pickwicks and its Wellers, Pendennises and Newcomes. Lord bless us! How the sun once shone on them. And with that, what a marvellous side procession to join from America, brought over in stately ships by Washington Irving and Fenimore Cooper, on rafts by Huck Finn, and as (first class) *Innocents Abroad,* by Mark Twain. On these, as on their British peers and predecessors, it seemed as if the illumination would never fail, and that there never could be a boy who hadn't heard of *Mr. Squeers* or a girl who hadn't wept over *Evangeline.*

And now, how great a change! It seems—so I am credibly informed and so I constantly notice—it seems that a great many of the young people of today (young people anywhere from six to sixty) have never heard of the *Knights of the Round Table,* or at least mix them up with *Ten Nights in a Barroom.* They think that Robin Hood was "Doug" Fairbanks when he was younger, and that Lady Godiva is the name of a flesh paint.

There is no need to get angry over it. No need, even for a professor, to lecture about it. The fact is that the world today is so closely interconnected on the surface, that it loses its connection downwards with the past. Let me try to say that more simply and then I'll get it better myself. In the world in which we live you may "sit in" at any aerial bombing going on in Barcelona or Shanghai, you can watch and hear the French people going crazy over King George VI, get all the wars in fifteen minutes, three wars going on and four practically guaranteed, get prize-fights, horse races, beauty shows—all hot and warm over the wire or the wireless and fused again into nothing in a moment, as printers melt up type to use the lead again, and so convert a sermon to a love story. Thus does the type of life melt and run over the radio and the cinema. Now I think we all get it.

And yet—even granting that this hurrying world exceeds and surpasses the older one, in its technique, immeasurably superior, in its possibilities of vivid depiction, its power of annihilating time and distance in the interest of narrative, and, perhaps, in many ways surpasses it in imaginative power—if only in its command of the grotesque, the lurid, the pathological forms of literary creation—grant all that, and yet something is irretrievably gone if we let go the thread of connection with the literature of the past.

We cannot live in a world of two dimensions, and literature, like life, must have its third. Our literature—common more or less, in its greatest sense, to all Western Europe, and laid as a present in the cradle of America—goes back hundreds and hundreds of years. It has to. It is a continuous growth. Mr. Pickwick, don't you see, is directly descended from Sir Roger de Coverley, and Charles O'Malley and Masterman Ready (never mind who they were: ask someone eighty years old), all such, and a host of heroes like them, are the Knights of the Round Table, still seeking for adventure. As the professorate would say, the continuity of a national literature is an essential condition of the continuation of national life.

Fetch me the old books and the old favourites—a whole real collection of them. I'll tell you what I'll do, if *you* will. I'll start all over again, beginning with the Trojan war, with Flaxman's illustrations, and then live over again the Last Days of Pompeii (look out for the lava, it's dangerous); we'll sit and watch the hundred coloured bannerets that flaunt in the breeze on the tourney ground of Ashby de la Zouche: drink sack with Falstaff; smoke long pipes with My Uncle Toby and Corporal Trim: and, in our heroic woods, wrap our colours round our breast (over our undershirt) on the fields of Spain, or climb the mast right up to the royal flush (I forget its exact name) and listen to the guns thunder on the deck below!

And, do you know, I think that such perusal, lost and absorbed in the fancied creature of which our own imagination must supply one half—and gives more than if we sit, full of peanuts and popcorn, allowing flickering shadows, created by someone else, and sound and melody, contrived by someone else, to fill us up with a story—as you feed porridge to a duck.

Fetch me the books. I'm going to read.

# What I Read Then—What You Read Now

*An Essay for the Young*

I AM sixty-eight years old. Sixty years ago, able to "read for myself," I first passed through that magic gateway into the Garden of Imagination. How greatly has it changed in sixty years to become the very different garden, the very different world that you young people know today.

The world in which I lived, as compared with yours, was vast and empty and voiceless. Look at the map of it as it hung on the walls of our schoolroom. There was Africa, a huge continent with nothing but an outside rim to it, rivers that seemed to come from nowhere, and queer names along the coast now mostly vanished—Mozambique, Zanzibar, Sofalá; Asia, a lot of it just about as empty, with a great desert smeared across the middle, with its northern coast, inaccessible and unknown, washing into the Arctic Sea. Over the heart of the continent were still inscribed such queer and romantic names as Turkestan and Bokhara and the Kurghis Steppes. Arabia was marked also as a great empty desert, closed and forbidden. Of our own continent, great stretches were still one vast emptiness of prairie and forest, the Rocky Mountains infinitely far away, as yet pierced only with the thin thread of two or three railway lines. Canada was huge and impenetrable. South America seemed on the map, as far as its insides went, an unexplored jungle.

In such a world, the sense of distance, of mystery and of the unknown was far more impressive than it is today. Your little world is shrunken, crowded—noisy and quarrelsome; it is like a street alley where there was once a silent wood.

I went the other day to the "pictures" and there before me on the screen was the young King Farouk of Egypt in a tarboosh and his Queen Farida in a Paris dress, just bowing themselves off in time to give the Japanese a chance to bomb Shanghai—also in a hurry, because Dartmouth was going to play hockey against McGill in a minute. The game was timed to allow Mussolini to come out on the roof of something or other (it went fast, I'm not sure what roof it was) and give a talk meant for Hitler, who appeared on the terrace of the Tiergarten—followed by the last minute of a fight in Madison Square Garden. . . . What a world! Rushing with voices that come from currents of cosmic force running through our very bodies themselves—quivering with power we cannot control, dangers we can see but not avoid.

I am not placing my world *above* yours—I am only exchanging one mystery for another. Our life, in any case, is framed in mystery, floating in the unknown; but the world of today seems to me, as an old man, in a way terrifying, like a thing rushing to its doom! But don't worry over that, my young friends! Old men have *always* thought the world was hurrying to its doom; and the joke is, it wasn't the *world* at all, but just the old men themselves.

But at least the contrast is great. Oh, to be back in the silent world of sixty years ago, in which a little boy with a book under an apple tree could be transported to the Rocky Mountains and there sit with Trapper Ben and Siwash Joe, beside a crackling fire of resinous pine, over a dish of buffalo meat. *You* can't sit there, you see, because if you did, Trapper Ben would say to Siwash Joe, "Turn on the radio, Joe, and let's hear what's doin'!" and Siwash Joe would say, "Me thinkum King Farouk of Egypt, he marry one nicey piece Squaw."

From such a setting you will easily understand that our reading of sixty years ago was based on the "bigness" and mystery of the world, of adventure in "distant lands" and "overseas," of people disappearing on long voyages to return as heroes or millionaires—back from the "diggings" or the "Cannibal Isles," or places like that. Notice the queer, fascinating names of our world. *You'd* call the "diggings" the "Consolidated Mining & Smelting Company," and the "Cannibal Isles" the "Municipality of Honolulu."

But of course we were strongest of all on "desert islands." The height of everybody's imagination was to share the fate of that lucky man Robinson Crusoe and be shipwrecked on a desert island, with one or two "other fellers"—no girls and no grown-ups. Desert islands always contained in abundance everything needed for life, liberty and the pursuit of happiness, such as breadfruit, yams, mangoes, cocoanuts—the stuff we never got at home except at Christmas. Of course the world's best desert island story was *Robinson Crusoe,* and no doubt you still read it. But it's really upside down. Defoe, who wrote it in 1719, meant it as a picture of loneliness and hardship, but the story, as stories do, turned into something else. Hence all boys envy Robinson his island and his goats and his parrot, and above all his man Friday. What they like is the fun of *being* there. When the Spaniards come into the story and the "adventures," the interest begins to fade.

The second best known desert story, written a hundred

years ago, was *Swiss Family Robinson*.  Its author was a
Swiss professor of philosophy so that shows how much *he*
knew about desert islands.  His story was no good after
you were ten years old—too namby-pamby, the Island too
easy.  And then how silly to have Mr. and Mrs. Robinson
there!  If you're lucky enough to hit on a desert island
you don't want your father and mother around.

But the best island story of the lot was Jules Verne's
*Mysterious Island*.  Verne was a Frenchman but the boys
of England and America adopted him so completely that
his books, as they appeared from about 1870 to 1900,
were put into English as soon as written.  Everybody has
heard of his "prophecy" stories, *Twenty Thousand Leagues
Under the Sea* and the *Clipper of the Clouds,* both come
true, and his *Journey to the Moon,* still waiting.  But best
of all was the wonderful island on which there lands a
group of castaways carried in a great storm in a balloon—
days and days in dark and wind and clouds, and blown
to land—heaven knows where, over such great spaces as
*we* knew and you can't *ever* know.  They are landed
empty-handed.  They begin as children of civilization,
from nothing, make and contrive everything, melting iron
for tools and mixing gunpowder—but *read* it!  *It's still
good*.

Of course our adventures turned mainly on the sea.
Say what you like, the sea can never be the same again
since steam and wireless and radio.

Where are now

> . . . *The Spanish sailors with bearded lips,*
> *And the mystery and beauty of the ships*
> *And the magic of the sea.*

Never again can be reproduced the wonder and beauty
of the great sailing ships outward bound in the sunset a

hundred years ago. Kipling has tried, in his *MacAndrew's Hymn,* to lift the huge floating machine called a steamship to a par with them in mystery and wonder. But it can't be done. The things are different. The one is man, the other is a machine.

Never again can literature have such a romantic basis as in those great days of the sea. You can read it now but it's all altered by your knowledge of radio and wireless. To you, all great sea stories suggest the idea, "What a pity they didn't have wireless!" But as for *us,* we just plunged from shipwreck to shipwreck, buffeted, tossed about, battered by a rush of nautical terms that we didn't understand! We saw the *Grosvenor* strike on the breakers and founder off the coast of South Africa—infinite desolation!—foundering with all hands—well, perhaps a few did reach shore to wander among the savages. We saw the Indiaman *Kent* burned to the water's edge, and the *Dunbar* beaten to pieces off Sydney Heads in the dark, and Masterman Ready in the wreck of the *Pacific.* Such writers as Captain Marryat, Fenimore Cooper and Clark Russell went literally around the world.

You can't read them now, my young friends, I am sure. But don't call them *slow;* the reason is not in them but in you. You are not—I say it very politely—fit to read them. You see, you are a child of machinery and electricity and so you want machinery at every turn. In my day, for example, in a sea story we used to "sweep the pirates off the deck with our cutlasses"; just a loud "Hurrah!" and over they went, still gnashing their teeth and biting their nails. But you would want to defeat them with "heat ray" or a "detonating bomb" or some such deviltry as that. Poor creatures! We just swept them off the deck— surely that doesn't hurt anybody.

But above all we loved the technical language of the

sea—the hundred ropes, every one with a name, and all the parts of the ship that we knew so well by name but only vaguely by location. The "bitts," the "main chains," the "scuppers"—were they parts of the "binnacle" or of the "taffrail"? The "tops," the "cross trees," the "main-royal-yard"—how high up are we?   Don't look down!

When your teachers teach you Shakespeare they explain to you what a wonderful knowledge of the sea Shakespeare had, just because of a little biff of sea language, or an attempt at it, in a play called *The Tempest*.

MASTER: *Good, speak to the mariners: fall to't yarely, or we run ourselves aground: bestir, bestir!*

BOATSWAIN: *Heigh, my hearts! Cheerly, cheerly, my hearts! yare, yare! Take in the topsail. Tend to the master's whistle. Down with the topsail. Yare!*

Tut! That's poor stuff, as Mark Train once showed (I am quoting his example)—just elementary. Compare it with the language of a *real* sailor like R. H. Dana, who wrote for us *Two Years Before the Mast.*

*Having hove short, cast off the gaskets, and made the bunt of each sail fast by the jigger, with a man on each yard, at a word the whole canvas on the ship was loosed, and with the greatest rapidity possible everything was sheeted home and hoisted up, the anchor tripped and cat-headed, and the ship under headway.*

But of course for *you* today there is no more "cat-heading" and "sheeting." Here is the kind of passage that *you* would expect in one of *your* books.

*Ned brought the radio message to the Captain. "A radio message, sir," he said, "in code."*

*"Decode it," cried Captain Carburetor. Ned, who was a skilled decoder, decoded the coded radio.*

"*What does it say, Ned?*" *asked the Captain.*

"*It's from an airplane, sir,*" *said Ned,* "*warning us that they can see an enemy submarine approaching us at a narrow angle.*"

"*How narrow?*" *asked Captain Carburetor.*

"*One degree, two minutes, log 5 ½,*" *answered Ned.*

"*How long have we got?*" *asked the Captain.*

"*Forty-six seconds, sir,*" *said Ned.*

"*Plenty!*" *said the Captain.* "*Pass me a depth bomb. Or here, boy,*" *he added, putting his hand, not unkindly, on the youngster's shoulder,* "*you jump over with it yourself.*"

But don't think for a moment that our adventure books were all and only of the sea. Not at all! We were just as much at home on land—in the heart of the forest or out on the prairie, with just enough savages "lurking" round to make things creepy. What they did was always called "lurking." They never came straight at you, in an open manly way; they "lurked." The only notice you got of their approach was the snapping of a dry twig; if you heard that, watch out! There was "a pesky redskin" somewhere around. Not that you yourself could hear it, but it was heard by the quick, trained ear of your guide and companion, Old Pigskin or Deerskin or whatever he was. I am thinking here, as you guess, perhaps, of Fenimore Cooper, whose books went all over the world in all the languages. Sixty years ago our continent was still young enough and open enough to keep Cooper's books near and intelligible; the prairie was still there and Sitting Bull's massacre of Custer's force recent enough to thrill us with its horror. It is strange to think of the marvellous vogue and influence of writers like Cooper, Scott and Dickens, writing for all the world. What *they* did can never be done again. The times forbid it. A writer nowadays may make a huge hit with a "best seller," *Gone with the Tide,* or *Off with the Wind*—half a million copies in a year, and in five years as dead and forgotten as dry grass.

Compare that with the world significance of *The Last of the Mohicans.* For the sake of *that* book, little boys in France and Germany dressed themselves up in what they meant for "leggings," with feathers and scalp-locks, and crawled around in the bushes of suburban gardens, avoiding the snapping of a dry twig. Remember the name if you don't know it already—*The Last of the Mohicans.* And don't pronounce it, as they *always* did in England, as if *Mohican* rhymed with "Joey can"; it's *Moheegan*—with a sort of Irish sound to it.

Later on, of course, we moved from pure adventure to adventure-romance—Walter Scott for all time the master of it. I am afraid that many young people, perhaps most, can't read Walter Scott today. They find him "too long-winded." That seems a queer accusation from a generation that makes its novels longer and longer, and thinks nothing of 600 pages. I admit that our books were "long-winded," but so are the books of today. Only they are long-winded in a different way. We took our "long wind" in the beginning, in the way of an introduction; nowadays you get the "long wind" all through; the book just goes on and on, like sawing wood. There's no *need* for it to stop; the end could be the beginning, just as in the moving pictures when we come in late and take a story backwards. We see the final death scene and then learn who it is that died and what killed him. In fact the "pictures" have shown us that a story is a circle. You begin anywhere.

But in *our* good old books you began at the beginning. Very much so. In fact, away before the beginning. If the story was laid in the Highlands you had to have first the history and description of the Highlands and how they got high. Then as the hero of the story was going to be Hoosh McQuoosh, you had to learn quietly and slowly all about the ancestry of the Hoosh McQuoosh family, one of whom fell at Bannockburn, one at Flodden—in fact they fell all over the place. But the reward was that by the time you got, slowly and gradually, into the story, you were right at home in it; it felt like part of you.

In one department I am willing to confess our books of sixty years ago were weak. That was in the matter of the heroines. I am afraid, as I look back at them, that our heroines were "simps." True, they were given large "lustrous eyes" like a startled fawn, mouths like "rosebuds" and a complexion that shot over with blushes as rapidly as a neon sign. But they were "simps." There was no sport in them. They wouldn't go out at night. If you dared to touch them, they cried out, "Unhand me, foul villain!" In fact their rhetoric—talk like *that*, only longer —was their strong point, their chief defence. Alone with a foul villain in a ruined castle they could blast him with it. Even in the forest they could knock out an Indian at ten yards. "Despicable Man," cried Ethelinda, as the fierce Mohawk raised his tomahawk, "alone and defenceless, beyond human help, a prey at once to treachery and menace, with nothing on which to rely save only the promptings of my own innocence, I command you to restrain your hand!" The Mohawk lowered his tomahawk with a groan; a blush as of shame (it really wasn't) mantled his dusky countenance, and with a couple more groans, he vanished into the brush!

When I compare those heroines with the kind of girls I see in the moving pictures today, skipping around on beaches and eating midnight suppers under rubber trees, I feel sorry to think what we missed!

But you must excuse my writing further—there's a film I must go to see—racketeers, gangsters, murders, trials, jails, all our bright new world spinning at its best.

# L'Envoi in Praise of the Americans

THE AMERICANS ARE A QUEER PEOPLE: THEY CAN'T REST. They have more time, more leisure, shorter hours, more holidays and more vacations than any other people in the world. But they can't rest. They rush up and down across their continent as tourists; they move about in great herds to conventions, they invade the wilderness, they flood the mountains, they keep hotels full. But they can't rest. The scenery rushes past them. They learn it but they don't see it. Battles and monuments are announced to them in a rubber-neck bus. They hear them but they don't get them. They never stop moving: they rush up and down as Shriners, Masons, Old Graduates, Veterans, Bankers,—they are a new thing each day, always rushing to a Reunion of something.

So they go on rushing till the undertaker gathers them in to a last convention.

. . . . . . . .

THE AMERICANS ARE A QUEER PEOPLE: THEY CAN'T READ. They have more schools, and better schools, and spend more money on schools and colleges than all of Europe. But they can't read. They print more books in one year than the French print in ten. But they can't read. They cover their country with 100,000 tons of Sunday newspapers every week. But they don't read them. They're too busy. They use them for fires and to make more paper with. They buy eagerly thousands of new novels at two dollars each. But they only read page one. Their streets are full of huge signs. They won't look at them. Their street cars are filled with advertising. They

324

turn their eyes away. Transparent colours, cartwheels and mechanical flares whirl and flicker in the crowded streets at night. No one sees them. Tons of circulars pour through the mails, through the houses and down the garbage chute. The last American who sat down to read died in about the days of Henry Clay.

· · · · · ·

THE AMERICANS ARE A QUEER PEOPLE: THEY CAN'T DRINK. All of the American nation is haunted. They have a fierce wish to be sober: and they can't. They pass fierce laws against themselves, shut themselves up, chase themselves, shoot themselves: and they can't stay sober and they can't drink. They have a furious idea that if they can ever get sober, all of them sober, they can do big things. But they can't hold it. They got this mentality straight out of home life in Ohio, copied from the wild spree and the furious repentance of the pioneer farmer. The nation keeps it yet. It lives among red spectres, rum devils, broken bottles, weeping children, penitentiary cells, barrooms and broken oaths. The last man who sat down and drank a quiet glass of beer, was found dead,—dead for twenty years,—in Milwaukee.

· · · · · ·

THE AMERICANS ARE A QUEER PEOPLE: THEY CAN'T PLAY. Americans rush to work as soon as they get up. They want their work as soon as they wake. It's a stimulant: the only one they're not afraid of. They used to open their offices at 10 o'clock: then at 9: then at 8: then at 7. Now they never shut them. Every business in America is turning into an open-all-day-and-night business. They eat all night, dance all night, build buildings all night, run cars all night, make a noise all night. They can't play. They try to, but they can't. They turn football into a fight, baseball into a lawsuit and yachting into machinery. They can't play. The little children can't play: they use mechanical toys instead: toy cranes hoisting toy loads: toy machinery spreading a toy industrial depression of infantile dulness. The grown-up people can't play: they use a mechanical gymnasium and a clockwork horse. They can't swim: they use a float. They can't run: they use a car. They can't laugh: they hire a comedian and watch him laugh.

·    ·    ·    ·    ·    ·    ·

THE AMERICANS ARE A QUEER PEOPLE: THEY DON'T GIVE A DAMN. All the world criticizes them and they don't give a damn. All the world writes squibs like this about them and they don't give a damn. Foreigner visitors come and write them up: they don't give a damn. Lecturers lecture at them: they don't care. They are told they have no art, no literature, and no soul. They never budge. Moralists cry over them, criminologists dissect them, writers shoot epigrams at them, prophets foretell the end of them, and they never move. Seventeen brilliant books analyze them every month: they don't read them. The Europeans threaten to unite against them: they don't mind. Equatorial Africa is dead sour on them: they don't even know it. The Chinese look on them as full of Oriental cunning: the English accuse them of British stupidity: the Scotch call them close-fisted: the Italians say they are liars: the French think their morals loose, and the Bolsheviks accuse them of communism.

·    ·    ·    ·    ·    ·    ·

But that's all right. The Americans don't give a damn: don't need to: never did need to. That is their salvation.